A Brief Guide to Molecular Mechanics and Quantum Chemical Calculations

Warren J. Hehre
Jianguo Yu
Philip E. Klunzinger
Liang Lou

D1604140

WAVEFUNCTION

Wavefunction, Inc.
18401 Von Karman Ave., Suite 370
Irvine, CA 92612

ISBN 1-890661-05-8

Printed in the United States of America

Acknowledgements

This book derives from materials and experience which have accumulated at Wavefunction over the past several years. It owes much to Wavefunction's members, both past and present. Special thanks goes to Bernard Deppmeier, Andy Driessen, Tom Hehre, Wayne Huang and Jeffrey Johnson. As always, Pamela Ohsan is thanked for turning our "sloppy manuscript" into a finished book.

Table of Contents

1. **Introduction** 1
   Potential Energy Surfaces 1
   Calculation Methods 3

2. **Theoretical Models** 7
   Molecular Mechanics 7
   Quantum Mechanics 10
      Born-Oppenheimer Approximation 11
      Hartree-Fock Approximation 12
      LCAO Approximation 12
      Roothaan-Hall Equations 13
      Correlated Models 14
         Møller-Plesset Models 14
         Density Functional Models 15
      Basis Sets for Hartree-Fock and MP2 Calculations 18
         STO-3G Minimal Basis Set 18
         3-21G, 6-31G and 6-311G Split-Valence Basis Sets 19
         6-31G*, 6-31G** and 6-311G* Polarization Basis
         Sets 20
         Basis Sets Incorporating Diffuse Functions 21
         3-21G$^{(*)}$ Basis Set 21
      Basis Sets for Density Functional Calculations 21
      Semi-Empirical Models 22
      Appendix A: Comparison of Self-Consistent and
                    Pertubative Becke-Perdew Models 23
      Appendix B: Comparison of Numerical and Gaussian
                    Basis Set Density Functional Models 28

3. **Selecting a Model** 35
   Equilibrium Geometries 36
   Reaction Energies 49
   Conformational Energy Differences 70

Transition-State Geometries and Activation Energies 77

Atomic Charges and Dipole Moments 90

Relative Computation Times for Models 94

Recommendations 97

4. **Using Models** 101

Using Approximate Equilibrium Geometries 102

Using Approximate Transition-State Geometries 107

Dealing with Flexible Molecules 109

Using Energy Data for Thermochemical and Kinetic
Comparisons 110

5. **Representative Applications** 115

Stabilizing Dewar Benzene 118

Protonation of Lysine 120

Stable Carbenes 122

Thermodynamic vs. Kinetic Control in Radical Cyclizations 124

Effect of Conformation on Rates of Diels-Alder Reactions . 126

6. **Graphical Models** 129

Molecular Orbitals 130

Electron Densities 133

Spin Densities 136

Electrostatic Potentials 138

Property Maps 139

Practical Considerations 144

7. **Applications of Graphical Models** 145

Structure of Benzene in the Solid State 146

Acidities of Carboxylic Acids 149

Stereochemistry of Base-Induced Elimination Reactions . 151

Stereochemistry of Nucleophilic Additions 154

Appendix   Common Terms and Acronyms 157

Index 165

Chapter 1

Introduction

Molecular mechanics calculations are routinely employed by chemists to establish molecular equilibrium geometries and conformations. Quantum chemical calculations, while significantly more costly, are also becoming common for these tasks, and also to supply quantitative thermochemical and kinetic data. More and more, calculations are being used not only to interpret experimental data, but also to supplement limited data or even replace it entirely.

Behind the increased usage of calculations among mainstream chemists are several factors. Most important, the theories underlying calculations have now evolved to a stage where a variety of important quantities, among them molecular equilibrium geometry and reaction energetics, may be obtained with sufficient accuracy to actually be of use. Closely related, are the spectacular advances in computer hardware over the past decade. "Good theories" may now be routinely applied to "real systems". Also, computer software has now reached a point where it can be easily used by chemists with little if any special training. Finally, computation ("molecular modeling") is now more and more being introduced into the core chemistry curriculum.[1] Much like NMR spectroscopy several decades ago, this will further its widespread use among future generations of chemists.

Potential Energy Surfaces

Most of the quantities of interest in a molecular modeling study (**equilibrium** and **transition-state geometries** and **conformations**, heats of reaction, **activation energies** and **vibrational frequencies**) follow directly from construction of a potential energy surface, that is, a plot of energy vs. **reaction coordinate**. One dimensional potential energy surfaces, are familiar to all chemists.

1

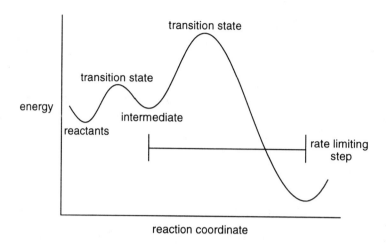

Collectively, energy minima and energy maxima are referred to as **stationary points**. Energy minima (or more precisely, **local minima**) correspond to stable molecules (reactants and products), although some energy minima may be too reactive to allow easy isolation and characterization (intermediates). The lowest energy local minimum is termed the **global minimum**. The positions of the energy minima along the reaction coordinate correspond to their equilibrium geometries, and their relative energies relate to their (relative) thermochemical stabilities. Thus, the overall process depicted above is exothermic, meaning that it is thermodynamically favorable.

Energy maxima on the potential energy surface correspond to **transition states**, and their positions along the reaction coordinate correspond to transition state geometries. These cannot be determined experimentally. The energies of the maxima relative to those of energy minima correspond to activation energies and may be related to reaction rates. "Real reactions" may involve several distinct steps (and one or more intermediates), and their overall rates are usually assumed to be that of the step which involves the highest-energy transition state (the "rate-limiting step").

Finally, the curvature of the potential energy surface in the vicinity of a minimum (as given by its second derivatives or **Hessian**) relates directly to a molecule's vibrational spectrum.

Calculation Methods

No one method of calculation is ideal for all applications, and a great deal of effort has been directed at finding suitable methods for different applications. Molecular mechanics methods[1] may easily be applied to molecules containing 1000 or more atoms. Recently developed mechanics force fields, such as MMFF94[2], provide quantitative descriptions of organic molecular structures and conformations, a vast improvement over earlier force fields such as SYBYL[3].

Among the quantum based methods which are least costly (and also least reliable) are so-called semi-empirical molecular orbital methods[4], including the popular MNDO[5] (MNDO/d[6]), AM1[7] and PM3[8,9] models. Semi-empirical models, which can be applied to molecules comprising upwards of 200 atoms, have proven to be quite successful for the calculation of equilibrium geometries, including the geometries of transition-metal inorganic and organometallic compounds, and moderately successful for the calculation of transition-state geometries. They are, however, not satisfactory for thermochemical and kinetic evaluations or for conformational assignments.

Hartree-Fock models[10] are, on the other hand, generally satisfactory for a wide variety of thermochemical and kinetic comparisons. They also provide an excellent account of molecular equilibrium and transition-state geometries, and a moderately successful account of equilibrium conformations. There are limitations and drawbacks to Hartree-Fock models. For one, they fare poorly for reactions involving explicit bond making or bond breaking, the most important being comparisons involving energy differences between reactants and transition states (as required for the calculation of absolute activation energies). Also, Hartree-Fock models have not met with much success in describing the structures of transition-metal inorganic and organometallic compounds. Finally, it should be noted that Hartree-Fock calculations increase in cost quite rapidly with increasing molecular size, and are usually not practical for molecules with more than 100 atoms.

The failure of Hartree-Fock models to properly account for the energetics of reactions involving bond making and bond breaking, and probably as well for the geometries of transition-metal compounds, can be traced to incomplete description of the coupling of motions of electrons ("electron correlation"). A number of correlated models, among the most popular, the MP2 model[10], have been developed. These generally provide excellent descriptions of equilibrium and transition-state geometries and conformations, as well as reaction thermodynamics and kinetics, including reactions where bonds are broken and formed. Correlated calculations such as MP2 are, however, much more costly than Hartree-Fock calculations, and are usually not practical for molecules with more than 20 atoms.

An alternative approach to the problem of electron correlation is found in so-called density functional models[11]. Instead of approximating the true many-electron solution by a composite of one-electron solutions, density functional models account explicitly for many-electron effects by "building in" a correlation term based on an "idealized" many-electron problem. Because many-electron effects are taken into account explicitly, the results of a density functional calculation should be superior to those from a Hartree-Fock treatment, and comparable to those from a "conventional" correlated calculation, such as an MP2 calculation. Even so, the computational cost involved in actually doing a density functional calculation actually increases more slowly with increasing molecular size than the cost of a Hartree-Fock or MP2 calculation. There are significant drawbacks with density functional models. Improvement of Hartree-Fock and correlated models such as MP2 follows in a straightforward manner by "easing" the approximations originally made to solve the correct many-electron problem. However, the only way that density functional models may be improved is to bring the "idealized" many-electron problem, on which the correlation term is based, closer to the "real" problem. Unfortunately, it is not yet obvious how to do this. Additionally, density functional models are not presently amenable to fully analytical treatments (as are Hartree-Fock and MP2 models). Required numerical integration steps introduce uncertainties into the calculations, and these need to be carefully monitored and controlled.

This brief guide focuses on the application of molecular mechanics models, semi-empirical and Hartree-Fock molecular orbital models, the MP2 model and density functional models, to the investigation of molecular structure and stability and chemical reactivity. It begins (**Chapter 2**) with a description of the theory underlying both molecular mechanics and quantum chemical techniques. Specific models are introduced representing the different classes of theory. The discussion is to some extent "superficial", insofar as it lacks both mathematical rigor and algorithmic details, although it does provide the essential framework on which practical models are constructed.

Comparison among specific molecular mechanics and quantum chemical models is provided in **Chapter 3**. Focus is on the ability of each model to reproduce known (experimental) equilibrium geometries and conformations, reaction energies and activation barriers, and dipole moments. Additionally, transition-state geometries obtained from different quantum chemical calculations are compared. While the number of individual comparisons is limited so as not to overwhelm the reader, it is sufficient to provide a reasonable overview of where each of the models is likely to be of value and where it is not.

Because each of the methods has its individual strengths and weaknesses, as well as its limitations, the best "strategies" for approaching "real problems" may involve not a single method, but rather a combination of methods. Specifically, simpler (less costly) methods may be able to provide equilibrium conformations and geometries for later energy and property calculations using higher-level (more costly) methods, without seriously affecting the overall quality of results. "Practical strategies" are explored in **Chapter 4**. As before, coverage is limited.[12]

Chapter 5 provides a small selection of "real problems" for which molecular mechanics and quantum chemical methods are well suited. These serve to illustrate strategies for combining the results of the different methods.

Chapter 6 introduces graphical models for describing molecular structure and properties, and for elucidating chemical reactivity and selectivity. These include electron and spin densities, the electrostatic potential, as well as the molecular orbitals themselves. Representative applications of graphical models are provided in **Chapter 7**.

A number of important topics are not touched on at all in this guide. Among these are methods accounting for solvent effects, methods for excited states and calculations of spectral quantities (IR, UV/vis and NMR).

This guide is tightly linked to the SPARTAN program[13], both insofar as the specific models illustrated, and with regard to the suggested "interplay" of models. Much of it applies to versions of SPARTAN for Macintosh and Windows 95/98/NT personal computers (MacSPARTAN and PC SPARTAN)[13].

References

1. For a recent example see: W.J. Hehre, A.J. Shusterman and J.E. Nelson, **The Molecular Modeling Workbook for Organic Chemistry**, Wavefunction, Inc., Irvine, CA, 1998.
2. M. Clark, R.D. Cramer III and N. van Opdensch, *J. Computational Chem.*, **10**, 982 (1989).
3. T.A. Halgren, *J. Computational Chem.*, **17**, 490 (1996); and following papers in this issue.
4. Reviews of semi-empirical methods: (a) T. Clark, **A Handbook of Computational Chemistry**, Wiley, New York 1986; (b) J.J.P. Stewart, *J. Computer Aided Molecular Design*, **4**, 1 (1990).
5. M.J.S. Dewar and W. Thiel, *J. Am. Chem. Soc.*, **99**, 4899 (1977).
6. W. Thiel and A. Voityuk, *Theor. Chim. Acta*, **81**, 391 (1992); W. Thiel and A.Voityuk, *Int. J. Quantum Chem.*, **44**, 807 (1992).
7. M.J.S. Dewar, E.G. Zoebisch, E.F. Healy and J.J.P. Stewart, *J. Am. Chem.* Soc., **107**, 3902 (1985).
8. J.J.P. Stewart, *J. Computational Chem.*, **10**, 209 (1989).
9. J. Yu and W.J. Hehre, to be published.
10. Review of Hartree-Fock and MP2 methods: W.J. Hehre, L. Radom, P.v.R. Schleyer and J.A. Pople, **Ab Initio Molecular Orbital Theory**, Wiley, New York, 1986.
11. Reviews of density functional theory: R.O. Jones and O. Gunnarsson, *Revs. Mod. Phys.*, **61**, 689 (1989); R.G. Parr and W. Yang, **Density Functional Theory of Atoms and Molecules**, Oxford Univ. Press, Oxford, 1989; J.K. Labanowski and J.W. Andzelm, Eds., **Density Functional Methods in Chemistry**, Springer-Verlag, New York, 1991.
12. Extended coverage may be found in: W.J. Hehre, **Practical Strategies for Electronic Structure Calculations**, Wavefunction, Inc., Irvine, CA, 1995.
13. SPARTAN, MacSPARTAN and PC SPARTAN are available from Wavefunction, Inc., Irvine, CA.

Chapter 2

Theoretical Models

This chapter describes the theoretical underpinnings of molecular mechanics calculations, Hartree-Fock and semi-empirical molecular orbital calculations, correlated MP2 and density functional calculations.

Molecular Mechanics[1]

Molecular mechanics describes molecules in terms of "connected atoms", and molecular geometry in terms of distortions from "ideal" bond distances, bond angles and dihedral angles, together with an account of nonbonded van der Waals and Coulombic interactions. The basic premise behind molecular mechanics is the high degree of transferability of geometrical parameters from one molecule to another, as well as predictable dependence of the parameters on atomic hybridization. For example, carbon-carbon single bond lengths generally fall in the small range from 1.45 to 1.55Å, and increase in length with increasing "p character" of the carbon hybrids. Thus, it is possible to provide a fairly accurate "guess" at molecular geometry in terms of bond lengths, bond angles and dihedral angles, provided that the molecule has already been represented in terms of a particular valence structure. The majority of organic molecules, and perhaps as well organometallic molecules, fall into this category.

Within the molecular mechanics framework, the "energy" of a molecule is described in terms of a sum of contributions arising from distortions from "ideal" bond distances ("stretch contributions"), bond angles ("bend contributions") and dihedral angles ("torsion contributions"), together with contributions due to "nonbonded" (van der Waals and Coulombic) interactions.

$$E^{total} = \overset{\text{bonds}}{\underset{i}{\sum}} E_i^{stretch} + \overset{\text{bond angles}}{\underset{i}{\sum}} E_i^{bend} + \overset{\text{dihedral angles}}{\underset{i}{\sum}} E_i^{torsion} + \overset{\text{nonbonded atoms}}{\underset{i}{\sum}\underset{j}{\sum}} E_{ij}^{nonbonded} \quad (1)$$

The first three summations in (1) are over all "bonds", all "bond angles" and all "dihedral angles", respectively, while the last summation is over all pairs of atoms which are not bonded.

Stretch and bend terms are most simply given in terms of quadratic ("Hook's law") forms.

$$E^{stretch}(r) = \frac{1}{2} k^{stretch}(r - r^{eq})^2 \quad (2)$$

$$E^{bend}(\alpha) = \frac{1}{2} k^{bend}(\alpha - \alpha^{eq})^2 \quad (3)$$

Here, r and α are the bond distance and angle, respectively, r^{eq} and α^{eq} are the "ideal" (equilibrium) bond length and bond angle, respectively, taken either from experiment or from quantum chemical calculations, and $k^{stretch}$ and k^{bend}, so-called stretch and bend "force constants", respectively, are parameters. Practical molecular mechanics methods may also include cubic and higher-order contributions, as well as "cross terms" to account for correlations between stretch and bend components.

Proper description of the torsion potential requires a form that reflects its inherent periodicity. For example, the three-fold periodicity of rotation about the carbon-carbon bond in ethane may be described by the functional form.

$$E^{torsion}(\omega) = k^{torsion3}[1 - \cos 3(\omega - \omega^{eq})] \quad (4)$$

Here, ω is the dihedral angle, ω^{eq} is the ideal dihedral angle and $k^{torsion3}$ is treated as a parameter. Bond torsion contributions to the overall energy also need to include terms which are one-fold and two-fold periodic.

$$E^{torsion}(\omega) = k^{torsion1}[1 - \cos(\omega - \omega^{eq})] + k^{torsion2}[1 - \cos 2(\omega - \omega^{eq})]$$

$$+ k^{torsion3}[1 - \cos 3(\omega - \omega^{eq})] \quad (5)$$

Here, $k^{torsion1}$ and $k^{torsion2}$ are additional parameters. Equation (5) is a truncated Fourier series.[2] Here, the one-fold term accounts for the difference in energy between *cis* and *trans* conformers, and the two-fold term accounts for the difference in energy between planar and perpendicular conformers. Practical molecular mechanics methods may also include higher-order terms, as well as terms accounting for asymmetrical environments.

Nonbonded interactions typically involve **van der Waals** (VDW) **interactions** and **Coulombic interactions**.

$$E^{nonbonded}(r) = E^{VDW}(r) + E^{Coulombic}(r) \qquad (6)$$

Most commonly, van der Waals interactions are represented as a sum of a repulsive and attractive terms.

$$E^{VDW}(r) = \varepsilon \left[\left(\frac{r^o}{r} \right)^{12} - 2 \left(\frac{r^o}{r} \right)^6 \right] \qquad (7)$$

Here, r is the nonbonded distance, and ε and r^o are parameters. This functional form results in a very steep energy barrier inside the sum of **van der Waals radii** for the two atoms involved, and a shallow energy well at larger separations, and as such accounts both for the inherent size requirements of atoms as well as for weak attractive forces between separated atoms.

The Coulombic term takes account of the interaction of charges.

$$E^{Coulombic}(r) = \frac{qq'}{r} \qquad (8)$$

Here again, r is the nonbonded distance, and the atomic charges, q, may either be treated as parameters or (more commonly) be taken from a quantum chemical calculation. In the latter case, the sum of atomic charges will equal the total molecular charge, 0 in the case of a neutral molecule.

Practical molecular mechanics models differ both in the number and specific nature of the terms which they incorporate, as well as in the details of their parameterization. Taken together, functional form and parameterization, constitute what is termed a **force field**. Very simple force fields such as **SYBYL**[3], developed by Tripos, Inc., may easily be extended to diverse systems but would not be expected to yield quantitatively accurate results. On the other hand, a model such as **MMFF94**[4], developed at Merck Pharmaceuticals, while limited in scope to common organic systems and biopolymers, is better able to provide quantitative accounts of molecular geometry and conformation.

Quantum Mechanics[5]

Quantum mechanics describes molecules in terms of interactions among nuclei and electrons, and molecular geometry in terms of minimum energy arrangements of nuclei. All quantum mechanical methods ultimately trace back to the **Schrödinger equation**, which for the special case of hydrogen atom (a single particle in three dimensions) may be solved exactly.

$$\left[\frac{-h^2}{8\pi^2 m} \nabla^2 - \frac{Ze^2}{r} \right] \psi(x,y,z) = E\psi(x,y,z) \tag{9}$$

Here, the quantity in square brackets represents the kinetic and potential energy of an electron of mass m a distance r from a nuclear charge Z (1 in hydrogen). h is Planck's constant and e is the electron charge. E is the energy of the electron, and ψ, a function of the atomic coordinates, is a **wavefunction** describing the motion of the electron as fully as possible. Wavefunctions for the hydrogen atom are the s, p, d... atomic orbitals, familiar to most chemists. The square of the wavefunction times a small volume gives the probability of finding the electron inside the volume. This is termed the **total electron density** (or more simply the **electron density**), and corresponds to the electron density measured in an X-ray diffraction experiment.

It is straightforward to generalize the Schrödinger equation to a multinuclear, multielectron system.

$$\hat{H}\Psi = E\Psi \tag{10}$$

Here, Ψ is a many-electron wavefunction and $\hat{H}$ is the so-called **Hamiltonian** operator (or more simply the Hamiltonian).

$$\hat{H} = \frac{-h^2}{8\pi^2} \sum_A^{\text{nuclei}} \frac{1}{M_A} \nabla_A^2 - \frac{h^2}{8\pi^2 m} \sum_a^{\text{electrons}} \nabla_a^2 - e^2 \sum_A^{\text{nuclei}} \sum_a^{\text{electrons}} \frac{Z_A}{r_{Aa}}$$

$$+ e^2 \sum_{A > B}^{\text{nuclei}} \frac{Z_A Z_B}{R_{AB}} + e^2 \sum_{a > b}^{\text{electrons}} \frac{1}{r_{ab}} \qquad (11)$$

The first two terms in (11) describe the kinetic energy of the nuclei, A, and the electrons, a, respectively, and the last three terms describe Coulombic interactions between particles. M are nuclear masses, and R_{AB}, r_{ab} and r_{Aa} are distances separating nuclei, electrons, and electrons and nuclei, respectively.

Unfortunately, the many-electron Schrödinger equation cannot be solved exactly (or at least has not been solved) even for the simplest many-electron system. Approximations need to be introduced to provide practical methods.

Born-Oppenheimer Approximation

One way to simplify the Schrödinger equation for molecular systems is to assume that the nuclei do not move. This is termed the Born-Oppenheimer approximation, and leads to an **"electronic"** **Schrödinger equation**.

$$\hat{H}^{el}\Psi^{el} = E^{el}\Psi^{el} \qquad (12)$$

$$\hat{H}^{el} = \frac{-h^2}{8\pi^2 m} \sum_a^{\text{electrons}} \nabla_a^2 - e^2 \sum_A^{\text{nuclei}} \sum_a^{\text{electrons}} \frac{Z_A}{r_{Aa}} + e^2 \sum_{a > b}^{\text{electrons}} \frac{1}{r_{ab}} \qquad (13)$$

The term in (11) describing the nuclear kinetic energy is missing in (13) (it is zero), and the nuclear-nuclear Coulomb term is a constant. It needs to be added to the electronic energy, E^{el}, to yield the total energy, E, for the system.

$$E = E^{el} + e^2 \sum_{A > B}^{\text{nuclei}} \frac{Z_A Z_B}{R_{AB}} \qquad (14)$$

Note that there is no reference to (nuclear) mass in the electronic Schrödinger equation. Mass effects (**isotope effects**) on molecular properties and chemical reactivities are of different origin.[6]

Even with the Born-Oppenheimer approximation, the Schrödinger equation is not solvable for more than a single electron. Additional approximations need to be made.

Hartree-Fock Approximation[7]

The most obvious simplification to the Schrödinger equation involves separation of variables, that is, replacement of the many-electron wavefunction by a product of one-electron wavefunctions. The simplest acceptable replacement, termed a **Hartree-Fock** or **single-determinant wavefunction**, involves a single determinant of products of one-electron functions, termed **spin orbitals**. Each spin orbital is written as a product of a space part, ψ, which is a function of the coordinates of a single electron and is referred to as a **molecular orbital**, and one of two possible spin parts, α or β. Only two electrons may occupy a given molecular orbital and they must be of opposite spin.

The Hartree-Fock approximation leads to a set of coupled differential equations (the **Hartree-Fock equations**), each involving a single electron. While they may be solved numerically, it is advantageous to introduce one additional approximation.

LCAO Approximation

This follows from the notion that the one-electron solutions for many-electron molecules will closely resemble the (one-electron) solutions for the hydrogen atom. This seems entirely reasonable. Since molecules are made up of atoms, why shouldn't molecular solutions be made up of atomic solutions? In practice, the molecular orbitals are expressed as linear combinations of a finite set (a **basis set**) of prescribed functions known as **basis functions**, ϕ.

$$\psi_i = \overset{\text{basis functions}}{\sum_{\mu}} c_{\mu i} \phi_\mu \tag{15}$$

c are the molecular orbital coefficients, often referred to simply (and incorrectly) as the molecular orbitals. Because the ϕ are usually centered at the nuclear positions (although they do not need to be), they are referred to as **atomic orbitals**, and expansion (15) is termed the Linear Combination of Atomic Orbitals or LCAO approximation.

Roothaan-Hall Equations[7]

The Hartree-Fock and LCAO approximations, taken together and applied to the electronic Schrödinger equation, lead to the Roothaan-Hall equations.

$$\sum_{\nu}^{\text{basis functions}} (F_{\mu\nu} - \varepsilon_i S_{\mu\nu}) c_{\nu i} = 0 \tag{16}$$

Here, ε are orbital energies, S is the overlap matrix (a measure of the extent to which basis functions "see each other"), and F is the Fock matrix, which is analogous to the Hamiltonian in the Schrödinger equation. In **atomic units** it is given by.

$$F_{\mu\nu} = (\phi_\mu | -\frac{1}{2}\nabla^2 - \sum_{A}^{\text{nuclei}} \frac{Z_A}{r_A} | \phi_\nu) + \sum_{\lambda}^{\text{basis functions}} \sum_{\sigma} P_{\lambda\sigma} \left[(\phi_\mu\phi_\nu | \phi_\lambda\phi_\sigma) - \frac{1}{2} (\phi_\mu\phi_\lambda | \phi_\nu\phi_\sigma) \right] \tag{17}$$

The first term in (17) accounts for the kinetic and potential energies of individual electrons, while the second term accounts for interactions among electrons. P is the so-called density matrix, the elements of which involve the square of the molecular orbital coefficients summed over all occupied molecular orbitals.

$$P_{\lambda\sigma} = 2 \sum_{i}^{\substack{\text{occupied} \\ \text{molecular orbitals}}} c_{\lambda i}^* c_{\sigma i} \tag{18}$$

Methods resulting from solution of the Roothaan-Hall equations are termed **Hartree-Fock** or ***Ab Initio* models**. The corresponding energy for an infinite (complete) basis set is termed the **Hartree-Fock energy**. The Hartree-Fock energy is not equal to the experimental energy.

Correlated Models

Hartree-Fock models treat the motions individual electrons as independent of one another. Because of this, electrons "get in each others way" to a greater extent than they should. This leads to overestimation of the electron-electron repulsion energy and to too high a total energy. **Electron correlation**, as it is termed, accounts for coupling of electron motions, and leads to a lessening of the electron-electron repulsion energy (and to a lowering of the overall total energy). The **correlation energy** is defined as the difference between the Hartree-Fock energy and the experimental energy.

Møller-Plesset Models[7]

A number of methods have been developed to account for electron correlation. With the exception of so-called density functional methods (see discussion following), these generally involve mixing the ground-state (Hartree-Fock) wavefunction with excited-state wavefunctions. Operationally, this entails implicit or explicit promotion of electrons from molecular orbtials which are occupied in the Hartree-Fock wavefunction to molecular orbitals which are unoccupied.

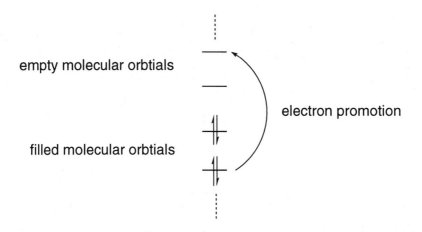

Among the simplest practical schemes are Møller-Plesset models which are formulated in terms of a generalized electronic Hamiltonian, $\hat{H}_\lambda$.

$$\hat{H}_\lambda = \hat{H}_o + \lambda\hat{V} \tag{19}$$

$\hat{H}_o$ is defined such that different states do not interact. The "perturbation" $\lambda\hat{V}$ is defined according to.

$$\lambda\hat{V} = \lambda(\hat{H} - \hat{H}_o) \qquad (20)$$

$\hat{H}$ is the correct Hamiltonian and λ is a dimensionless parameter. ψ_λ and E_λ, the wavefunction and energy for a system described by the Hamiltonian $\hat{H}_\lambda$, may then be expanded in powers of λ, i.e.

$$\psi_\lambda = \psi^{(0)} + \lambda\psi^{(1)} + \lambda^2\psi^{(2)} + \ldots \qquad (21)$$

$$E_\lambda = E^{(0)} + \lambda E^{(1)} + \lambda^2 E^{(2)} + \ldots \qquad (22)$$

The **Møller-Plesset energy** to first order is the Hartree-Fock energy. The second-order Møller Plesset energy, $E^{(2)}$, is given by.

$$E^{(2)} = \overset{\substack{\text{molecular orbitals} \\ \text{filled} \quad \text{empty}}}{\sum_{i < j} \sum \sum_{a < b} \sum} (\varepsilon_a + \varepsilon_b - \varepsilon_i - \varepsilon_j)^{-1}[(ij \parallel ab)]^2 \qquad (23)$$

ε_i, ε_j are energies of filled molecular orbitals, ε_a, ε_b energies of empty molecular orbitals, and integrals $(ij \parallel ab)$ account for changes in electron-electron interactions as a result of promotion.

Møller-Plesset theory terminated to second-order, or **MP2**, is perhaps the simplest model based on electron promotion which offers improvement over Hartree-Fock theory. Higher-order models (MP3, MP4, etc.) have been formulated, but in practice are limited in application to very small systems.

Density Functional Models[8]

Density functional models provide an alternative approach to the treatment of correlation in many-electron systems. They follow from a theorem, which states that the minimal energy of a collection of electrons under the influence of an external (Coulombic) field is a unique "functional" (a function of a function) of the electron density. To see how this theorem is put to practical use, first consider the energy of a many-electron system as given by Hartree-Fock theory.

$$E^{HF} = E^{nuclear} + E^{core} + E^{Coulomb} + E^{exchange} \qquad (24)$$

Here, $E^{nuclear}$ accounts for Coulombic repulsion of nuclei, E^{core} for both electron kinetic energy and Coulombic attraction between electrons and nuclei, and $E^{Coulomb}$ for Coulombic repulsion of electrons. $E^{exchange}$ also involves electron-electron interactions, and has the effect of reducing the size of the Coulomb term.

The energy according to density functional theory includes the same nuclear, core and Coulomb terms as the Hartree-Fock energy, yet replaces the Hartree-Fock exchange energy by an exchange functional, $E^X(P)$, and adds a correlation functional, $E^C(P)$.

$$E^{DFT} = E^{nuclear} + E^{core} + E^{Coulomb} + E^X(P) + E^C(P) \qquad (25)$$

Both of the latter are functions of the electron density, P. The simplest models are called **local spin density** or **local density models**, and will be referred to as **SVWN (Slater, Vosko, Wilk, Nusair) models**. Here, the form of the exchange and correlation functionals follows from the exact (numerical) solution of a many-electron gas of uniform density, as a function of the density, by subtracting E^{core} and $E^{Coulomb}$ from the total energy (there is no $E^{nuclear}$ term).

The SVWN model would not be expected to be satisfactory for molecular systems where the electron density is non-uniform. The model may be improved by introducing explicit dependence on the gradient of the electron density, in addition to the density itself. Such procedures are termed **gradient-corrected** or **non-local density functional** models. An obvious way to do this, for the case where the density is a "slowly varying function", is in terms of a simple power-series expansion. Unfortunately, such an approach leads to divergent behavior in the limit of large density gradients. An alternative is the so-called generalized gradient approximation proposed by Becke and Perdew.[9]

In the **Becke-Perdew (BP or BP86) model**, a new potential is used in place of the local potential in the self-consistent-field (SCF) procedure. This actually comprises a local part and a gradient correction. The latter needs to be recalculated at every SCF iteration. An alternative, and computationally simpler approach, is to introduce the gradient correction only after convergence based on the local

16

potential alone has been achieved. This procedure, referred to as a perturbative Becke-Perdew model (or **pBP**), offers significant computational advantages over the corresponding self-consistent procedure. As shown in **Appendix A** to this chapter, it yields nearly identical structures and relative energies to the full self-consistent BP model, and will be used throughout this guide.

The equations which result from both local density and self-consistent Becke-Perdew formulations may be solved iteratively by expanding the set of one-particle wavefunctions in terms of a set of basis functions centered on the individual nuclei. Note, however, that terms associated with the exchange and correlation functionals typically involve forms for which analytical expressions of the required integrals are either not available, or would be too complicated to deal with were they available. It is usually necessary to resort to numerical integration techniques. Because of this, calculated quantities show larger uncertainties than those from Hartree-Fock and MP2 models. Total (and relative) energies should be accurate to 0.0002 hartrees (on the order of a tenth of a kcal/mol) and bond lengths accurate to 0.005Å.

Because density functional models take electron correlation into account in an explicit manner, resulting properties should more closely mirror those of conventional correlated models, such as the MP2 model, than those of Hartree-Fock models. That is to say, density functional results should be "better" than those from Hartree-Fock models. Because the energy is expressed as a function of a single "variable" (the electron density), the equations which result from application of density functional theory are conceptually simpler than those resulting from Hartree-Fock theory (where the "variables" are the set of one-electron wavefunctions). In fact, a density functional calculation scales (formally) as the cube of molecular size, compared to a (formal) fourth power dependence on size for a Hartree-Fock calculation. (In practice, both density functional and Hartree-Fock calculations scale more slowly than the formal rules suggest, see **Chapter 3**, in particular, **Table 3-22**.)

Basis Sets for Hartree-Fock and MP2 Calculations

For practical reasons, Hartree-Fock and MP2 calculations make use of basis sets of Gaussian-type functions. These are closely related to exact solutions of the hydrogen atom, and comprise a polynomial in the Cartesian coordinates (x,y,z) followed by an exponential in r^2. Several series of Gaussian basis sets have now received widespread use and are thoroughly documented. Underlying these, are minimal (STO-3G) and split-valence (3-21G, 6-31G and 6-311G) representations. These may be supplemented by sets of polarization and/or diffuse functions.

STO-3G Minimal Basis Set[10]

The simplest possible atomic orbital representation is termed a minimal basis set. This comprises only those functions required to accommodate all of the electrons of the atom, while still maintaining its overall spherical symmetry. In practice, this involves a single (1s) function for hydrogen and helium, and a set of five functions (1s, 2s, $2p_x$, $2p_y$, $2p_z$) for lithium to neon. Note that, while 2p functions are not occupied in the lithium and beryllium atoms, they are required to provide proper descriptions in molecules.

Each of the basis functions in the STO-3G representation is expanded in terms of three Gaussians, where the values of the Gaussian exponents and the linear coefficients have been determined by least squares as best fits to Slater-type (exponential) functions.

There are two obvious shortcomings of a minimal basis set. The first is that all basis functions are either themselves spherical (s functions) or come in sets which, taken together, describe a sphere (p functions). As a consequence, molecules which incorporate only atoms with "spherical environments" or "nearly spherical environments" will be better described than molecules which incorporate atoms with "aspherical environments".

The second shortcoming follows from the fact that basis functions are atom centered. While this is not absolutely necessary, there are no other obvious (unambiguous) locations for the basis functions. The choice of atom-centered locations for the basis functions does, however, restrict their flexibility to describe electron distributions between nuclei ("bonds").

3-21G[11], 6-31G[12] and 6-311G[13] Split-Valence Basis Sets

The first shortcoming of a minimal basis set may be resolved by providing two sets of valence basis functions ("inner" and "outer" functions). For example, proper linear combinations (α and β are the molecular orbital coefficients to be determined in the the solution of the Roothaan-Hall equations) allow for the fact that the p orbitals which make up a "tight" σ bond need to be more contracted than the p orbitals which make up a "looser" π bond.

$$p_\sigma = \alpha \; \text{⬡} \; + \; \beta \; \text{⬡} \; \Rightarrow \; \text{⬡}$$

$$p_\pi = \alpha \; \text{⬡} \; + \; \beta \; \text{⬡} \; \Rightarrow \; \text{⬡}$$

A split-valence basis set represents inner-shell atomic orbitals by a single set of functions, and valence atomic orbitals by two sets of functions. Thus, hydrogen is represented by two s-type functions, and main-group elements are provided two complete sets of valence s and p functions.

Among the simplest split-valence basis sets are 3-21G and 6-31G. Each inner-shell atomic orbital in the 3-21G basis set is represented by a single function, which in turn is written in terms of three Gaussians, while basis functions representing inner and outer components of valence atomic orbitals are written in terms of expansions of 2 and 1 Gaussians, respectively. 6-31G basis sets are similarly constructed, with inner-shell orbitals represented in terms of six Gaussians and valence orbitals split into three and one Gaussian components.

A higher level of valence shell splitting is possible. 6-311G basis sets represent inner-shell atomic orbitals in terms of six Gaussians, but split the valence functions into three parts instead of two, these being written in terms of three, one and one Gaussians, respectively.

Expansion coefficients and Gaussian exponents for (3-21G, 6-31G and 6-311G representations have been determined by energy minimization on atomic ground states. In the case of 6-311G representations, minimizations have been carried out at the MP2 level rather than at the Hartree-Fock level.

6-31G*, 6-31G** and 6-311G* Polarization Basis Sets[14]

The second shortcoming of a minimal (or split-valence) basis set may be resolved by providing d-type functions on main-group heavy atoms, and (optionally) p-type functions on hydrogen. This allows displacement of electron distributions away from the nuclear positions.

This can be thought about either in terms of "hybrid orbitals", e.g., pd and sp hybrids as shown above, or alternatively in terms of a Taylor series expansion of a function (d functions are the first derivatives of p functions, p functions are the first derivatives of s functions, etc.).

A polarization basis set represents inner-shell atomic orbitals by a single set of functions and valence-shell atomic orbitals by two (or more) sets of functions, and a includes set of d-type **polarization functions** on main-group elements and (optionally) a set of p-type polarization functions on hydrogen.

Among the simplest polarization basis sets are 6-31G* and 6-311G*, constructed from 6-31G and 6-311G, respectively, by adding a set of six d-type Gaussians for each heavy (non-hydrogen) atom. Orbital exponents for polarization functions have been chosen to give the lowest energies for representative molecules. Polarization of the s orbitals on hydrogen atoms is necessary for an accurate description of the bonding in many systems (particularly those in which hydrogen is a bridging atom). The 6-31G** basis set is identical to 6-31G*, except that it provides p-type polarization functions for hydrogen.

Basis Sets Incorporating Diffuse Functions[15]

Calculations involving anions, e.g., absolute acidity calculations, often pose special problems, and may require basis sets to be supplemented by **diffuse functions** (designated by "+" as in **6-31+G*** and **6-311+G****). Here, only heavy atoms are provided diffuse (s and p-type) functions, although it is also possible to supplement hydrogens as well.

3-21G$^{(*)}$ Basis Set[16]

Experience suggests that d-type functions are required on second-row and heavier main-group elements even though they are not occupied in the free atoms. (This situation is very much like that found for alkali and alkaline earth elements where p-type functions, while not occupied in the ground-state atoms, are required for proper description of bonding in molecules.) This applies not only to molecules with expanded valence octets (so-called "hypervalent molecules") but also to normal-valent systems. One basis set which has proven to be quite successful for molecules incorporating heavy main-group elements is 3-21G$^{(*)}$, constructed from 3-21G basis sets by the addition of a set of d-type functions on second-row and heavier main-group elements only. Reference to 3-21G in this guide implies use of 3-21G$^{(*)}$ for second-row and heavier main-group elements.

Basis Sets for Density Functional Calculations

Unlike Hartree-Fock and MP2 models, which utilize Gaussian basis sets, the density functional models in SPARTAN use tabulated atomic solutions, supplemented by d-type functions on heavy atoms and (optionally) p-type functions on hydrogen. Numerical polarization ("*") and full polarization ("**") basis sets are referred to as **DN*** and **DN****, respectively, leading to SVWN/DN*, SVWN/DN**, pBP/DN* and pBP/DN** models. In practice, the "outer" component of the valence description follows from solution of the neutral atom, while the "inner" (more contracted) component follows from solution of the corresponding +2 atomic ion.

Comparison between results obtained from density functional calculations using numerical and Gaussian basis sets are provided in

Appendix B to this chapter. These show that numerical basis sets are generally "superior" (insofar as convergence toward the limits of the model) to Gaussian basis sets of the "same size".

Semi-Empirical Models[17]

Semi-empirical models follow directly from Hartree-Fock models. First, the size of the problem is reduced by restricting treatment to valence electrons only (electrons associated with "inner shells" are considered to be part of a fixed "core"). Next, the basis set is restricted to a minimal representation. For main-group elements, this comprises a single s-type function and a set of p-type functions, e.g., 2s, $2p_x$, $2p_y$, $2p_z$ for a first-row element, and for transition metals, a set of d-type functions, an s function and a set of p functions, e.g., $3d_{x^2-y^2}$, $3d_{z^2}$, $3d_{xy}$, $3d_{xz}$, $3d_{yz}$, 4s, $4p_x$, $4p_y$, $4p_z$ for first-row transition metals. Hydrogen is represented by a single (1s) function. The only exception to this is the **MNDO/d** method[18] for second-row (and heavier) main-group elements, used in conjunction with **MNDO**[19] for hydrogen and first-row elements. This incorporates a set of d-type functions, in direct analogy to 3-21G$^{(*)}$ used in conjunction with 3-21G.

The central approximation, in terms of reducing overall computation, is to insist that atomic orbitals residing on different atomic centers do not overlap.

$$\int \phi_\mu \phi_\nu d\tau = 0 \qquad \phi_\mu \text{ and } \phi_\nu \text{ not on the same atom} \qquad (26)$$

This is referred to as the **N**eglect of **D**iatomic **D**ifferential **O**verlap or **NDDO approximation**, and reduces the number of electron-electron interaction terms from $O(N^4)$ in the Roothaan-Hall equations to $O(N^2)$, where N is the total number of basis functions.

Additional approximations are introduced in order to further simplify the overall calculation, and more importantly to provide a framework for the introduction of empirical parameters. Except for models for transition metals, semi-empirical parameterizations are based on reproducing a wide variety of experimental data, including equilibrium geometries, heats of formation, dipole moments and ionization potentials. Parameters for **PM3** for transition metals are based only on reproducing equilibrium geometries. The **AM1**[20] and PM3[21,22] models incorporate essentially the same approximations but differ in their parameterization.

Appendix A: Comparison of Self-Consistent and Pertubative Becke-Perdew Models

Non-local correlations can be introduced into density functional models either self consistently or in a perturbative manner. The latter is favored from the standpoint of "cost", and is the basis for the models employed throughout this guide. It is important, therefore, to assess the magnitudes of any errors which might arise due to use of pertubative models in lieu of self-consistent models.

Comparisons of equilibrium and transition-state geometries from pBP and BP density functional models using the DN** numerical basis set are provided in **Tables 2-1** and **2-2**, respectively. The largest difference in equilibrium bond lengths from the two procedures is 0.004Å, and the mean absolute deviation of BP from pBP bond distances is only 0.002Å. Mean absolute errors for the two models are identical. Bond distances in transition states show similar fluctuations.

A comparison of reaction energetics from both pBP/DN** and BP/DN** models is provided in **Table 2-3**. As with geometry comparisons, the two sets of results are nearly identical (the largest difference is only 1 kcal/mol), and the mean absolute deviation between BP and pBP models is significantly smaller than the mean absolute error (in relation to experiment) of either model. A similar story applies to conformational energy differences (**Table 2-4**), where the two sets of BP/DN** calculations yield nearly identical results.

Calculated activation energies also appear to be insensitive to the manner in which non-local density corrections are introduced (**Table 2-5**). The largest difference in absolute activation energies between pBP/DN** and BP/DN** models is only 1 kcal/mol.

Overall there appears to be little reason to employ the (more costly) self-consistent procedure to introduce non-local corrections for equilibrium and transition-state geometry calculations, as well as for

Table 2-1: Comparison of Bond Distances from Perturbed and Fully Self-Consistent BP/DN** Calculations (Å)

bond	molecule	pBP/DN**	BP/DN**	expt.
C-C	propyne	1.456	1.456	1.459
	propene	1.501	1.500	1.501
	cyclopropane	1.511	1.509	1.510
	propane	1.541	1.539	1.526
	cyclobutane	1.558	1.555	1.548
C=C	cyclopropene	1.301	1.299	1.300
	propene	1.343	1.340	1.318
	cyclopentadiene	1.362	1.359	1.345
C≡C	propyne	1.217	1.213	1.206
C-N	formamide	1.366	1.366	1.376
	trimethylamine	1.459	1.460	1.451
	aziridine	1.478	1.482	1.475
C-O	formic acid	1.359	1.361	1.343
	dimethyl ether	1.426	1.427	1.410
	oxirane	1.442	1.444	1.436
C=O	acetone	1.224	1.223	1.222
mean absolute deviation		0.002	–	–
mean absolute error		0.009	0.009	–

Table 2-2: Comparison of Bond Distances in Transition States from Perturbed and Fully Self-Consistent BP/DN** Calculations (Å).

reaction		pBP/DN**	BP/DN**
	r_1	1.79	1.81
	r_2	1.82	1.81
	r_3	1.20	1.20
	r_1	1.41	1.40
	r_2	1.32	1.31
	r_3	1.34	1.33
	r_4	1.28	1.28
	r_5	1.27	1.27
	r_6	2.04	2.05
mean absolute deviation		0.01	–

Table 2-3: Comparison of Reaction Energies from Perturbed and Fully Self-Consistent BP/DN Calculations (kcal/mol)**

reaction	pBP/DN**	BP/DN**	expt.[a]
bond dissociation reactions			
$CH_3\text{-}CH_3 \rightarrow 2CH_3^{\cdot}$	93	94	88
$CH_3\text{-}NH_2 \rightarrow CH_3^{\cdot} + NH_2^{\cdot}$	89	89	83
$CH_3\text{-}OH \rightarrow CH_3^{\cdot} + OH^{\cdot}$	97	97	92
$CH_3\text{-}F \rightarrow CH_3^{\cdot} + F^{\cdot}$	115	114	111
hydrogenation reactions			
$CH_3\text{-}CH_3 + H_2 \rightarrow 2CH_4$	-19	-19	-19
$CH_3\text{-}NH_2 + H_2 \rightarrow CH_4 + NH_3$	-27	-27	-26
$CH_3\text{-}OH + H_2 \rightarrow CH_4 + H_2O$	-30	-30	-30
$CH_3\text{-}F + H_2 \rightarrow CH_4 + HF$	-28	-28	-29
$H_2C=CH_2 + 2H_2 \rightarrow 2CH_4$	-58	-58	-57
$HC\equiv CH + 3H_2 \rightarrow 2CH_4$	-109	-109	-105
isomerization reactions			
acetaldehyde $\rightarrow$ oxirane	26	26	26
propyne $\rightarrow$ cyclopropene	21	21	22
propene $\rightarrow$ cyclopropane	7	7	7
acetone $\rightarrow$ oxetane	32	32	31
bond separation reactions			
$CH_3CH=CH_2 + CH_4 \rightarrow CH_3CH_3 + CH_2=CH_2$	5	5	5
$CH_3CHO + CH_4 \rightarrow CH_3CH_3 + H_2CO$	11	11	11
$NH_2CHO + CH_4 \rightarrow CH_3NH_2 + H_2CO$	34	34	30
△ $+ 3CH_4 \rightarrow 3CH_3CH_3$	-21	-22	-22
△(NH) $+ 2CH_4 + NH_3 \rightarrow CH_3CH_3 + 2CH_3NH_2$	-16	-17	-17
△(O) $+ 2CH_4 + H_2O \rightarrow CH_3CH_3 + 2CH_3OH$	-12	-12	-14
mean absolute deviation	0	–	–
mean absolute error	2	2	–

a) G2 results replace experimental data for bond dissociation energies. See reference 23.

Table 2-4: Comparison of Conformational Energy Differences from Perturbed and Fully Self-Consistent BP/DN** Calculations (kcal/mol)

molecule	low energy/ high energy conformer	pBP/DN**	BP/DN**	expt.
n-butane	*trans/gauche*	1.2	1.4	0.77
1-butene	*skew/cis*	0.4	0.2	0.2
1,3-butadiene	*trans/gauche*	3.9	4.1	1.7>2,2.5
acrolein	*trans/cis*	2.2	2.2	2.0,2.06
formic acid	*cis/trans*	4.5	4.5	3.90
methyl ethyl ether	*anti/gauche*	1.5	1.3	1.5
methyl vinyl ether	*cis/skew*	1.8	1.6	1.7
cyclohexane	*chair/twist boat*	6.8	6.9	5.5
methycyclohexane	*equatorial/axial*	1.8	2.0	1.8
mean absolute deviation		0.1	–	–
mean absolute error		0.5	0.6	–

Table 2-5: Comparison of Activation Energies from Perturbed and Fully Self-Consistent BP/DN Calculations (kcal/mol)**

reaction	pBP/DN**	BP/DN**	expt.
$CH_3NC \longrightarrow CH_3CN$	40	40	38
$HCO_2CH_2CH_3 \longrightarrow HCO_2H + C_2H_4$	42	42	40,44
(cyclohexadiene isomerization)	27	27	36
(oxygen-containing ring isomerization)	21	21	31
(cyclopentadiene + ethylene → norbornene)	17	16	20
(retro-ene → diene + C_2H_4)	48	48	–
(lactone → diene + CO_2)	32	32	–
(sulfolene → diene + SO_2)	19	19	–
mean absolute deviation	0	–	–

thermochemical and activation energy calculations. Note, however, that because non-local corrections introduced following convergence of the local density model affect only the energy, and not the electron density, properties based on the density, such as the dipole moment, will not "be corrected". Here, sizable differences between BP and pBP models might be expected. However, as shown by the comparisons in **Table 2-6** differences between pBP/DN** and BP/DN** dipole moments for compounds incorporating heteroatoms are quite small, and significantly less than the differences with experimental moments.

Appendix B: Comparison of Numerical and Gaussian Basis Set Density Functional Models

A comparison of bond lengths from non-local density (BP) calculations with 6-31G* and 6-311G* Gaussian basis sets and with the DN* numerical basis set is provided in **Table 2-7**. The latter is the "same size" as the 6-31G* basis set, and smaller than the 6-311G* basis set, which involves additional valence-shell splitting. In general, all geometries are very similar, with DN* structures usually being closer to those from 6-311G* Gaussian basis set calculations. Differences in bond lengths among the different methods are typically smaller than errors in relation to experiment.

Comparison of the results of numerical and Gaussian basis set BP density functional calculations for the energetics of bond dissociation reactions, hydrogenation reactions, isomerization reactions and bond separation reactions is provided in **Table 2-8**. As with structure comparisons, energetic results for numerical and Gaussian basis sets are all similar. Deviations with BP/DN* are typically largest for comparisons involving the 6-31G* Gaussian basis set, and otherwise never greater than a few kcal/mol. In most (but not all) cases, BP/DN* calculations yield energies which are closest to those resulting from the larger Gaussian basis set. There is really no difference in the "quality" (relative to experiment) between BP density functional calculations with Gaussian and numerical basis sets.

Conformational energy differences are dealt with in **Table 2-9**. The (experimental) energy differences dealt with here are typically very

Table 2-6: Comparison of Dipole Moments for Molecules Incorporating Heteroatoms from Perturbed and Fully Self-Consistent BP/DN** Calculations (debyes)

molecule	pBP/DN**	BP/DN**	expt.
NH_3	1.78	1.77	1.47
NMe_3	0.53	0.56	0.61
H_2O	2.08	2.01	1.85
Me_2O	1.31	1.32	1.30
(oxirane)	2.02	1.99	1.89
PH_3	0.80	0.72	0.58
PMe_3	1.19	1.18	1.19
H_2S	1.31	1.23	0.97
Me_2S	1.55	1.56	1.50
(thiirane)	1.92	1.94	1.85
(dihydrothiophene)	0.39	0.40	0.55
mean absolute deviation	0.03	–	–
mean absolute error	0.15	0.12	–

Table 2-7: Comparison of Bond Distances from BP Calculations with Gaussian and Numerical Basis Sets (Å)

bond	molecule	6-31G*	6-311G*	DN*	expt.
C-C	propyne	1.462	1.458	1.455	1.459
	propene	1.506	1.503	1.498	1.501
	cyclopropane	1.516	1.515	1.510	1.510
	propane	1.536	1.534	1.529	1.526
	cyclobutane	1.559	1.559	1.554	1.548
C=C	cyclopropene	1.306	1.302	1.298	1.300
	propene	1.343	1.339	1.339	1.318
	cyclopentadiene	1.361	1.358	1.356	1.345
C≡C	propyne	1.219	1.213	1.213	1.206
C-N	formamide	1.370	1.369	1.366	1.376
	trimethylamine	1.461	1.460	1.462	1.451
	aziridine	1.484	1.483	1.480	1.475
C-O	formic acid	1.360	1.357	1.359	1.343
	dimethyl ether	1.418	1.419	1.420	1.410
	oxirane	1.441	1.441	1.441	1.436
C=O	acetone	1.227	1.220	1.224	1.222
mean absolute deviation		0.004	0.003	–	–
mean absolute error		0.010	0.007	0.007	–

Table 2-8: Comparison of Reaction Energies from BP Calculations with Gaussian and Numerical Basis Sets (kcal/mol)

reaction	6-31G*	6-311G*	DN*	expt.[a]
bond dissociation reactions				
$CH_3\text{-}CH_3 \rightarrow 2CH_3^\cdot$	99	98	95	88
$CH_3\text{-}NH_2 \rightarrow CH_3^\cdot + NH_2^\cdot$	93	93	90	83
$CH_3\text{-}OH \rightarrow CH_3^\cdot + OH^\cdot$	101	100	97	92
$CH_3\text{-}F \rightarrow CH_3^\cdot + F^\cdot$	119	117	116	111
hydrogenation reactions				
$CH_3\text{-}CH_3 + H_2 \rightarrow 2CH_4$	-18	-18	-18	-19
$CH_3\text{-}NH_2 + H_2 \rightarrow CH_4 + NH_3$	-23	-24	-24	-26
$CH_3\text{-}OH + H_2 \rightarrow CH_4 + H_2O$	-23	-27	-26	-30
$CH_3\text{-}F + H_2 \rightarrow CH_4 + HF$	-18	-19	-25	-29
$H_2C=CH_2 + 2H_2 \rightarrow 2CH_4$	-60	-59	-57	-57
$HC\equiv CH + 3H_2 \rightarrow 2CH_4$	-115	-110	-108	-105
isomerization reactions				
acetaldehyde $\rightarrow$ oxirane	25	27	26	26
propyne $\rightarrow$ cyclopropene	19	21	21	22
propene $\rightarrow$ cyclopropane	6	7	7	7
acetone $\rightarrow$ oxetane	31	32	32	31
bond separation reactions				
$CH_3CH=CH_2 + CH_4 \rightarrow CH_3CH_3 + CH_2=CH_2$	6	5	5	5
$CH_3CHO + CH_4 \rightarrow CH_3CH_3 + H_2CO$	11	11	11	11
$NH_2CHO + CH_4 \rightarrow CH_3NH_2 + H_2CO$	35	36	34	30
(cyclopropane) $+ 3CH_4 \rightarrow 3CH_3CH_3$	-24	-24	-23	-22
(aziridine, NH) $+ 2CH_4 + NH_3 \rightarrow CH_3CH_3 + 2CH_3NH_2$	-19	-18	-18	-17
(oxirane, O) $+ 2CH_4 + H_2O \rightarrow CH_3CH_3 + 2CH_3OH$	-15	-15	-13	-14
mean absolute deviation	2	1	–	–
mean absolute error	5	4	2	–

a) G2 results replace experimental data for bond dissociation energies. See reference 23.

31

Table 2-9: Comparison of Conformational Energy Differences from BP Calculations with Gaussian and Numerical Basis Sets (kcal/mol)

molecule	low energy/ high energy conformer	6-31G*	6-311G*	DN*	expt.
n-butane	*trans/gauche*	0.8	0.8	1.3	0.77
1-butene	*skew/cis*	0.3	0.3	0.4	0.2
1,3-butadiene	*trans/gauche*	3.7	3.7	3.8	1.7>2,2.5
acrolein	*trans/cis*	1.8	1.7	2.1	2.0,2.06
formic acid	*cis/trans*	5.0	5.3	4.5	3.90
methyl ethyl ether	*anti/gauche*	1.2	1.4	1.3	1.5
methyl vinyl ether	*cis/skew*	2.5	2.4	2.3	1.7
cyclohexane	*chair/twist boat*	6.4	6.2	6.8	5.5
methycyclohexane	*equatorial/axial*	2.2	2.1	2.6	1.8
mean absolute deviation		0.3	0.3	–	–
mean absolute error		0.6	0.5	0.6	–

small, and some buildup of error in the numerical density functional calculations might be expected. However, only small deviations are noted between numerical and Gaussian basis set calculations.

Activation energies for a series of organic reactions are considered in **Table 2-10**. All results are similar, and the largest deviations are only a few kcal/mol. Neither Gaussian nor numerical basis set calculations yields "better" results in comparison with experiment.

References

1. Review of molecular mechanics methods: U. Burkert and N.L. Allinger, **Molecular Mechanics**, ACS monograph 177, American Chemical Society, Washington D.C., 1982.
2. L. Radom, W.J. Hehre and J.A. Pople, *J. Amer. Chem. Soc.,* **94**, 2371 (1972).
3. M. Clark, R.D. Cramer III and N. van Opdensch, *J. Computational Chem.,* **10**, 982 (1989).
4. T.A. Halgren, *J. Computational Chem.,* **17**, 490 (1996), and following papers.
5. Reviews of basic quantum mechanics: I.N. Levine, **Quantum Chemistry**, 4th ed., Prentice Hall, Englewood Cliffs, NJ, 1991; P.W. Atkins and R.S. Friedman, **Molecular Quantum Mechanics**, 3rd ed., Oxford Univ. Press, Oxford, 1997.
6. For an excellent discussion of isotope effects see: N. Isaacs, **Physical Organic Chemistry**, 2nd Ed., Longman Scientific and Technical, 1995, p.286.
7. Review of Hartree-Fock and Møller-Plesset models: W.J. Hehre, L. Radom, P.v.R. Schleyer and J.A. Pople, *Ab Initio* **Molecular Orbital Theory**, Wiley, New York, 1986.
8. Reviews of density functional theory: R.O. Jones and O. Gunnarsson, *Revs. Mod. Phys.,* **61**, 689 (1989); R.G. Parr and W. Yang, **Density Functional Theory of Atoms and Molecules**, Oxford Univ. Press, Oxford, 1989; J.K. Labanowski and J.W. Andzelm, Eds., **Density Functional Methods in Chemistry**, Springer-Verlag, New York, 1991.
9. A.D. Becke, *Phys. Rev. A,* **38**, 3089 (1988); J.P. Perdew, *Phys. Rev. B,* **33**, 8822 (1986).
10. W.J. Hehre, R.F. Stewart and J.A. Pople, *J. Chem. Phys.,* **51**, 2657 (1969), and following papers.
11. J.S. Binkley, J.A. Pople and W.J. Hehre, *J. Chem. Soc.,* **102**, 939 (1980), and following papers.
12. W.J. Hehre, R. Ditchfield and J.A. Pople, *J. Chem. Phys.,* **56**, 2257 (1972), and following papers.
13. R. Krishnan, M.J. Frisch and J.A. Pople, *J. Chem.Phys.,* **72**, 4244 (1980).
14. P.C. Hariharan and J.A. Pople, *Chem. Phys. Lett.,* **66**, 217 (1972), and following papers.
15. T. Clark, J. Chandrasekhar, K. Spitznagel and P.v.R. Schleyer, *J. Computational Chem.,* **4**, 294, (1983).
16. W.J. Pietro, M.M. Francl, W.J. Hehre, D.J. DeFrees, J.A. Pople and J.S. Binkley, *J. Am. Chem. Soc.,* **104**, 5039 (1982), and following papers.
17. Reviews of semi-empirical methods: (a) T. Clark, **A Handbook of Computational Chemistry**, Wiley, New York 1986; (b) J.J. P. Stewart, *J. Computer Aided Molecular Design,* **4**, 1 (1990).
18. W. Thiel and A. Voityuk, *Theor. Chim. Acta.,* **81**, 391 (1992); W. Thiel and A. Voityuk, *Int. J. Quantum Chem.,* **44**, 807 (1992).
19. M.J.S. Dewar and W. Thiel, *J. Am. Chem. Soc.,* **99**, 4899 (1977).
20. M.J.S. Dewar, E.G. Zoebisch, E.F. Healy and J.J.P. Stewart, *J. Am. Chem.* Soc., **107**, 3902 (1985).
21. J.J.P. Stewart, *J. Computational Chem.,* **10**, 209 (1989).
22. J. Yu and W.J. Hehre, to be published.
23. L.A. Curtiss, K. Raghavari, G.W. Trucks and J.A. Pople, *J. Chem Phys.,* **94**, 7221 (1991).

Table 2-10: Comparison of Activation Energies from BP Calculations with Gaussian and Numerical Basis Sets (kcal/mol)

reaction	6-31G*[a]	6-311G*[a]	DN*	expt.
$CH_3NC \longrightarrow CH_3CN$	37	37	40	38
$HCO_2CH_2CH_3 \longrightarrow HCO_2H + C_2H_4$	46	42	44	40,44
(cyclohexadiene → cyclohexadiene)	28	28	27	36
(pyran rearrangement)	22	22	21	31
(cyclopentadiene + ethylene → norbornene)	12	14	15	20
(cyclohexene → diene $+$ C_2H_4)	50	48	50	–
(pyranone $=$ O → diene $+$ CO_2)	34	31	32	–
(sulfolene SO_2 → diene $+$ SO_2)	18	15	20	–
mean absolute deviation	2	2	–	–

a) Assumes HF/6-31G* reactant and transition-state geometries.

Chapter 3
Selecting a Model

This chapter considers two issues central to selecting an appropriate model: performance and cost. The performance of SYBYL and MMFF94 molecular mechanics models, MNDO (MNDO/d), AM1 and PM3 semi-empirical molecular orbital models, Hartree-Fock models with STO-3G, 3-21G⁽⁾, 6-31G*, 6-31G**, 6-31+G*, 6-311G* and 6-311+G** basis sets, the MP2/6-31G* model and local and non-local (Becke-Perdew) density functional models with the DN* and DN** basis sets, for the calculation of equilibrium geometries, reaction energies, conformational energy differences, transition-state geometries and activation energies, and dipole moments is documented first. Next, estimates of relative computation times for the various methods are provided. Together, these data allow selection of an appropriate model for the problem at hand.*

The success of any particular model depends first on its ability to consistently reproduce known (experimental) data. In the case of semi-empirical and Hartree-Fock molecular orbital models, MP2 models and density functional models, these are structural data, energy data relating to reaction thermochemistry and kinetics, as well as energy differences among stable conformers, and data relating to molecular charge distributions reflected in dipole moments. With the exception of dipole moments from the MMFF94 model, molecular mechanics models are applicable only to the description of equilibrium geometries and conformational energy differences, and must be judged on this basis alone. Success is not an absolute judgement. Different properties, and certainly different problems, may require different levels of confidence to actually be of value.

Unfortunately, success alone is not sufficient. A model also needs to be "practical" for the task at hand. What is practical and what is not is also not an absolute judgement. The nature (size) of the problem needs to be taken into account, as do the available computational resources and the "patience" of the practitioner. Practical models usually do share one feature in common, in that they are not likely to be the "best possible" treatments which have been formulated. Compromise is almost always an essential component of model selection.

The performance and "cost" of a variety of models are dealt with in this chapter. Specifically, these are the SYBYL and MMFF94 molecular mechanics models, MNDO(MNDO/d), AM1 and PM3 semi-empirical models, Hartree-Fock models with STO-3G, 3-21G$^{(*)}$, 6-31G*, 6-31G**, 6-31+G*, 6-311G* and 6-311+G** basis sets, the MP2/6-31G* model, and local (SVWN) and Becke-Perdew (pBP) density functional models with the DN* and DN** basis sets. Hartree-Fock models beyond the popular 6-31G* model have been chosen to assess the individual effects of polarization functions on hydrogen (6-31G**), of diffuse functions (6-31+G*), and of additional valence-shell splitting (6-311G*), as well as a combination of the three (6-311+G**).

The material which follows is divided first according to question: "How well do the models reproduce what is known?" and "How costly are the models in comparison with alternative techniques?". The response to the first question is divided according to property: equilibrium geometries, reaction energetics, conformational energy differences, transition-state geometries and activation energies, and dipole moments. The response to the second question is in terms of relative computation times for single energy calculations and geometry optimizations on different size molecules.

Equilibrium Geometries

Carbon-carbon bond lengths in hydrocarbons obtained from molecular mechanics calculations, semi-empirical calculations, Hartree-Fock calculations, MP2 calculations, and density functional calculations are compared with experimental values in **Table 3-1**.

All models perform moderately well, both in reproducing absolute bond lengths and in properly ordering bond distances. This includes molecular mechanics schemes and the three semi-empirical molecular orbital models, all of which are much less costly to apply than the other methods addressed here. Both classes of methods appear to be suitable for equilibrium structure determination. The mean absolute error resulting from MMFF94 molecular mechanics calculations is half of that from SYBYL mechanics, while MNDO and PM3 semi-empirical calculations yield slightly smaller errors than AM1 calculations.

Hartree-Fock, MP2 and density functional methods also provide a good account of hydrocarbon bond lengths. Note, that Hartree-Fock bond lengths with the 6-31G* and larger basis sets are consistently shorter than experimental distances. This is easily rationalized. Treatment of electron correlation involves promotion of electrons from filled molecular orbitals (in the Hartree-Fock wavefunction) to empty molecular orbitals. As the filled molecular orbitals which make up the description of hydrocarbons are (generally) net bonding in character, and as unfilled molecular orbitals are (generally) net antibonding in character, any promotions should result in bond weakening, i.e.

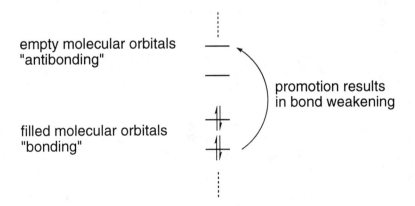

Addition of polarization functions on hydrogen, addition of diffuse functions and further splitting of the valence shell has little effect on the performance of the 6-31G* model for hydrocarbon geometries. That is to say, the 6-31G* model appears to accurately reflect the properties of the Hartree-Fock limit insofar as hydrocarbon bond lengths.

Table 3-1: Bond Lengths in Hydrocarbons (Å)

bond	molecule	molecular mechanics		semi-empirical			Hartree-Fock				
		SYBYL	MMFF94	MNDO	AM1	PM3	STO-3G	3-21G	6-31G*	6-31G**	6-31+G*
C-C	but-1-yne-3-ene	1.441	1.419	1.417	1.405	1.414	1.459	1.432	1.439	1.439	1.440
	propyne	1.458	1.463	1.445	1.427	1.433	1.484	1.466	1.468	1.467	1.469
	trans-1,3-butadiene	1.478	1.442	1.466	1.451	1.456	1.488	1.479	1.467	1.468	1.468
	propene	1.509	1.493	1.496	1.476	1.480	1.520	1.510	1.503	1.502	1.503
	cyclopropane	1.543	1.502	1.526	1.501	1.499	1.502	1.513	1.497	1.497	1.499
	propane	1.551	1.520	1.530	1.507	1.512	1.541	1.541	1.528	1.528	1.528
	cyclobutane	1.547	1.543	1.549	1.543	1.542	1.554	1.571	1.548	1.545	1.545
C=C	cyclopropene	1.317	1.302	1.328	1.318	1.314	1.277	1.282	1.276	1.276	1.278
	allene	1.305	1.297	1.306	1.298	1.297	1.288	1.292	1.296	1.296	1.299
	propene	1.339	1.339	1.340	1.331	1.328	1.308	1.316	1.318	1.318	1.322
	cyclobutene	1.327	1.345	1.355	1.354	1.349	1.314	1.326	1.322	1.322	1.325
	but-1-yne-3-ene	1.338	1.337	1.345	1.336	1.332	1.320	1.320	1.322	1.321	1.325
	trans-1,3-butadiene	1.338	1.338	1.344	1.335	1.331	1.313	1.320	1.323	1.322	1.326
	cyclopentadiene	1.335	1.341	1.362	1.359	1.352	1.319	1.329	1.329	1.328	1.332
C≡C	propyne	1.204	1.201	1.197	1.197	1.192	1.170	1.188	1.187	1.187	1.190
	but-1-yne-3-ene	1.201	1.200	1.198	1.198	1.193	1.171	1.190	1.189	1.189	1.191
mean absolute error		0.024	0.011	0.012	0.016	0.014	0.021	0.013	0.012	0.012	0.011

bond	molecule	Hartree-Fock		MP2	density functional				expt.
		6-311G*	6-311+G**	6-31G*	SVWN/DN*	SVWN/DN**	pBP/DN*	pBP/DN**	
C-C	but-1-yne-3-ene	1.438	1.438	1.429	1.406	1.406	1.422	1.422	1.431
	propyne	1.466	1.466	1.463	1.438	1.438	1.456	1.456	1.459
	trans-1,3-butadiene	1.467	1.467	1.458	1.437	1.437	1.455	1.456	1.483
	propene	1.502	1.502	1.499	1.479	1.479	1.500	1.501	1.501
	cyclopropane	1.500	1.500	1.504	1.493	1.494	1.509	1.511	1.510
	propane	1.527	1.528	1.526	1.508	1.510	1.538	1.541	1.526
	cyclobutane	1.546	1.546	1.545	1.538	1.534	1.556	1.558	1.548
C=C	cyclopropene	1.275	1.276	1.303	1.292	1.293	1.300	1.301	1.300
	allene	1.294	1.295	1.313	1.303	1.303	1.313	1.313	1.308
	propene	1.318	1.320	1.338	1.330	1.331	1.342	1.343	1.318
	cyclobutene	1.322	1.323	1.347	1.340	1.340	1.349	1.350	1.332
	but-1-yne-3-ene	1.321	1.322	1.344	1.338	1.339	1.350	1.351	1.341
	trans-1,3-butadiene	1.322	1.324	1.344	1.338	1.338	1.349	1.350	1.345
	cyclopentadiene	1.328	1.330	1.354	1.349	1.350	1.361	1.362	1.345
C≡C	propyne	1.184	1.185	1.220	1.210	1.210	1.216	1.217	1.206
	but-1-yne-3-ene	1.186	1.187	1.223	1.213	1.214	1.220	1.220	1.208
	mean absolute error	0.012	0.012	0.008	0.015	0.014	0.010	0.011	–

Correlated MP2/6-31G*, pBP/DN* and pBP/DN** models do not show the same systematic error in bond lengths as do Hartree-Fock models, and calculated distances are neither consistently shorter nor consistently longer than experimental values. On the other hand, local density SVWN/DN* and SVWN/DN** models typically lead to bond distances which (like those from Hartree-Fock models) are shorter than experimental values. The explanation for this is not apparent.

While supporting data have not been provided, it needs to be emphasized that correlated (MP2 and density functional) models require basis sets which incorporate d-type (polarization) functions. Whereas Hartree-Fock models need only to describe molecular orbitals which are occupied (s and p-type orbitals in the case of organic molecules), correlated models also need proper descriptions of unoccupied orbitals which may involve d-type functions.

Similar conclusions follow from comparison of calculated and experimental C-N, C-O and C=O bond distances (**Table 3-2**). All models provide a credible account. As with hydrocarbons, both Hartree-Fock and local density models lead to bond lengths which are typically shorter than experimental distances, while MP2 and pBP models lead to bond lengths which are longer. Both of the latter provide a somewhat better account of bond distances in these compounds than do molecular mechanics models, semi-empirical and Hartree-Fock molecular orbital models or local density functional models.

Calculations involving second-row elements in both normal-valent and hypervalent molecules show much wider variations (**Table 3-3**). SYBYL molecular mechanics performs poorly, while the MMFF94 mechanics model does better. The AM1 semi-empirical model performs poorly, whereas both MNDO (MNDO/d) and PM3 models perform reasonably well. The similar performance of MNDO/d and PM3 suggests that addition of d-functions on second row elements in semi-empirical models (MNDO/d) may be no more important than improved parameterization (PM3).

The STO-3G model performs very poorly, especially for hypervalent molecules. On the other hand, the performance of 3-21G$^{(*)}$ and, to a greater extent, larger-basis-set Hartree-Fock models, is exceptional for these compounds (far better than the performance of the same models for hydrocarbons and molecules incorporating heteroatoms). The explanation is not apparent.

While supporting data have not been supplied, it needs to be emphasized that accurate descriptions of the geometries of molecules incorporating second-row (and heavier main-group) elements requires inclusion of d-type functions in the basis set (for the second-row elements). In their absence, calculated bond distances are much too long.

The MP2/6-31G* model and the two local density functional models all lead to similar results (not quite as good as the Hartree-Fock models but much better than any of the semi-empirical models). On the other hand, pBP/DN* and pBP/DN** models do not perform as well. Bond lengths in hypervalent molecules are sometimes overestimated by several tenths of an Å. The reason is not clear, although one possibility is that f-type functions need to be added to the basis sets for these elements.

Calculated bond lengths in cations and anions are compared with experimental values in **Table 3-4**. Precise comparisons are not possible. The experimental data derives from solid-state structures (gas-phase experimental geometries of ions are not available), and would be expected to depend on the counterion. However, the experimental data are certainly good enough to allow general conclusions to be drawn regarding performance of the various models.

SYBYL molecular mechanics performs poorly for charged systems and cannot be recommended. MMFF94 does much better, although it has been parameterized only for a few "biologically important" ions.

The three semi-empirical models provide a relatively good account of bond lengths in charged systems. The mean absolute error resulting from the PM3 calculations is the smallest, and that from MNDO calculations the largest. However the differences are not great.

STO-3G calculations give a poor account of both cation and anion bond distances, although the remaining Hartree-Fock models give good accounts. 6-31G* and larger-basis-set models yield nearly

41

Table 3-2: Bond Lengths in Molecules Incorporating Heteroatoms (Å)

bond	molecule	molecular mechanics		semi-empirical			Hartree-Fock				
		SYBYL	MMFF94	MNDO	AM1	PM3	STO-3G	3-21G	6-31G*	6-31G**	6-31+G*
C-N	formamide	1.346	1.360	1.389	1.367	1.392	1.436	1.353	1.349	1.348	1.348
	methyl isocyanide	1.500	1.426	1.424	1.395	1.433	1.447	1.432	1.421	1.422	1.423
	trimethylamine	1.483	1.462	1.464	1.445	1.480	1.486	1.464	1.445	1.445	1.446
	aziridine	1.484	1.459	1.479	1.455	1.484	1.482	1.491	1.449	1.448	1.449
	nitromethane	1.458	1.488	1.546	1.500	1.514	1.531	1.493	1.479	1.478	1.481
C-O	formic acid	1.334	1.348	1.354	1.357	1.344	1.385	1.350	1.323	1.322	1.322
	dimethyl ether	1.437	1.421	1.396	1.417	1.406	1.433	1.433	1.391	1.392	1.393
	methanol	1.437	1.416	1.391	1.411	1.395	1.433	1.441	1.400	1.399	1.402
	oxirane	1.395	1.433	1.418	1.436	1.432	1.433	1.470	1.402	1.402	1.403
C=O	formamide	1.219	1.221	1.227	1.243	1.220	1.216	1.212	1.193	1.193	1.195
	formic acid	1.220	1.217	1.227	1.230	1.211	1.214	1.198	1.182	1.182	1.184
	formaldehyde	1.220	1.225	1.217	1.217	1.222	1.217	1.207	1.184	1.184	1.189
	acetaldehyde	1.221	1.229	1.221	1.232	1.210	1.217	1.209	1.188	1.188	1.189
	acetone	1.221	1.230	1.227	1.235	1.216	1.219	1.211	1.192	1.192	1.194
mean absolute error		0.024	0.011	0.024	0.016	0.015	0.021	0.012	0.020	0.020	0.019

bond	molecule	Hartree-Fock		MP2	density functional				expt.
		6-311G*	6-311+G**	6-31G*	SVWN/DN*	SVWN/DN**	pBP/DN*	pBP/DN**	
C-N	formamide	1.349	1.349	1.362	1.350	1.349	1.367	1.366	1.376
	methyl isocyanide	1.423	1.424	1.426	1.396	1.397	1.418	1.419	1.424
	trimethylamine	1.445	1.446	1.455	1.437	1.434	1.457	1.459	1.451
	aziridine	1.450	1.450	1.474	1.454	1.454	1.507	1.507	1.475
	nitromethane	1.481	1.484	1.488	1.474	1.476	1.507	1.507	1.489
C-O	formic acid	1.321	1.321	1.351	1.336	1.336	1.359	1.359	1.343
	dimethyl ether	1.389	1.391	1.416	1.393	1.395	1.424	1.426	1.410
	methanol	1.398	1.400	1.424	1.406	1.406	1.435	1.436	1.421
	oxirane	1.399	1.400	1.438	1.415	1.416	1.441	1.442	1.436
C=O	formamide	1.187	1.188	1.225	1.214	1.215	1.225	1.226	1.193
	formic acid	1.176	1.177	1.214	1.202	1.203	1.211	1.212	1.202
	formaldehyde	1.178	1.180	1.221	1.202	1.203	1.212	1.213	1.208
	acetaldehyde	1.182	1.183	1.224	1.209	1.209	1.219	1.220	1.216
	acetone	1.187	1.188	1.228	1.215	1.216	1.224	1.224	1.222
mean absolute error		0.020	0.020	0.007	0.014	0.015	0.011	0.011	–

Table 3-3: Bond Lengths in Molecules Incorporating Second-Row Elements (Å)

bond	molecule	molecular mechanics		semi-empirical			Hartree-Fock				
		SYBYL	MMFF94	MNDO	AM1	PM3	STO-3G	3-21G(*)	6-31G*	6-31G**	6-31+G*
C-Si	vinylsilane	1.871	1.833	1.841	1.762	1.813	1.852	1.867	1.873	1.873	1.876
	tetramethylsilane	1.877	1.875	1.891	1.829	1.890	1.863	1.889	1.894	1.893	1.894
C-P	trimethylphosphine oxide	1.800	1.755	1.842	1.648	1.824	1.840	1.805	1.819	1.818	1.818
	trimethylphosphine	1.830	1.834	1.832	1.725	1.782	1.841	1.848	1.853	1.852	1.852
C-S	thiophene	1.781	1.712	1.729	1.672	1.725	1.732	1.722	1.726	1.725	1.725
	dimethylsulfone	1.801	1.776	1.809	1.690	1.793	1.814	1.756	1.774	1.773	1.774
	dimethylsulfoxide	1.803	1.809	1.819	1.739	1.818	1.809	1.791	1.796	1.795	1.797
	dimethyl sulfide	1.820	1.808	1.794	1.751	1.801	1.796	1.813	1.809	1.808	1.808
	thiirane	1.812	1.725	1.817	1.791	1.821	1.774	1.817	1.812	1.811	1.812
	methane thiol	1.821	1.804	1.792	1.754	1.801	1.798	1.823	1.817	1.817	1.818
C-Cl	trichloromethane	1.767	1.772	1.782	1.786	1.779	1.808	1.776	1.763	1.763	1.763
	tetrachloromethane	1.767	1.782	1.786	1.760	1.747	1.818	1.778	1.767	1.766	1.766
	dichloromethane	1.767	1.767	1.779	1.741	1.758	1.803	1.784	1.768	1.768	1.769
	chloromethane	1.767	1.767	1.780	1.741	1.764	1.802	1.802	1.785	1.785	1.786
P=O	trimethylphosphine oxide	1.566	1.370	1.497	1.462	1.482	1.620	1.478	1.474	1.474	1.476
S=O	dimethylsulfone	1.450	1.450	1.500	1.399	1.468	1.851	1.438	1.437	1.437	1.438
	dimethylsulfoxide	1.447	1.500	1.519	1.491	1.557	1.820	1.490	1.485	1.485	1.490
S-F	sulfur tetrafluoride (*eq*)	1.800	–	1.642	1.545	1.596	1.675	1.550	1.544	1.544	1.543
	sulfur tetrafluoride (*ax*)	1.800	–	1.697	1.573	1.622	1.675	1.617	1.632	1.632	1.641
mean absolute error		0.039	0.023	0.026	0.052	0.024	0.072	0.011	0.007	0.007	0.006

bond	molecule	Hartree-Fock		MP2	density functional				expt.
		6-311G*	6-311+G**	6-31G*	SVWN/DN*	SVWN/DN**	pBP/DN*	pBP/DN**	
C-Si	vinylsilane	1.871	1.873	1.869	1.848	1.848	1.874	1.876	1.853
	tetramethylsilane	1.888	1.888	1.889	1.861	1.862	1.891	1.893	1.875
C-P	trimethylphosphine oxide	1.815	1.815	1.820	1.794	1.796	1.828	1.827	1.813
	trimethylphosphine	1.850	1.849	1.852	1.826	1.829	1.860	1.861	1.841
C-S	thiophene	1.724	1.724	1.718	1.702	1.702	1.729	1.729	1.714
	dimethylsulfone	1.774	1.774	1.785	1.764	1.764	1.803	1.803	1.777
	dimethylsulfoxide	1.797	1.797	1.785	1.794	1.794	1.836	1.838	1.799
	dimethyl sulfide	1.808	1.808	1.806	1.787	1.789	1.827	1.829	1.802
	thiirane	1.814	1.814	1.817	1.799	1.801	1.833	1.834	1.815
	methane thiol	1.818	1.818	1.817	1.799	1.802	1.837	1.839	1.819
C-Cl	trichloromethane	1.764	1.764	1.766	1.758	1.759	1.790	1.791	1.758
	tetrachloromethane	1.768	1.768	1.771	1.764	1.764	1.795	1.795	1.767
	dichloromethane	1.771	1.770	1.769	1.759	1.760	1.797	1.798	1.772
	chloromethane	1.790	1.789	1.778	1.765	1.768	1.803	1.805	1.781
P=O	trimethylphosphine oxide	1.470	1.471	1.507	1.485	1.485	1.500	1.500	1.479
S=O	dimethylsulfone	1.430	1.431	1.469	1.442	1.442	1.458	1.459	1.431
	dimethylsulfoxide	1.483	1.486	1.512	1.485	1.486	1.503	1.504	1.485
S-F	sulfur tetrafluoride (*eq*)	1.534	1.534	1.588	1.578	1.578	1.606	1.606	1.545
	sulfur tetrafluoride (*ax*)	1.640	1.643	1.665	1.661	1.660	1.700	1.700	1.646
mean absolute error		0.006	0.006	0.013	0.012	0.011	0.026	0.027	–

Table 3-4: Bond Lengths in Cations and Anions (Å)

cation/anion	bond	molecular mechanics		semi-empirical			Hartree-Fock				
		SYBYL	MMFF94	MNDO	AM1	PM3	STO-3G	3-21G	6-31G*	6-31G**	6-31+G*
(structure)	CN	1.357	1.328	1.363	1.376	1.380	1.355	1.324	1.322	1.321	1.322
(structure)	CC	1.395	—	1.412	1.394	1.385	1.377	1.361	1.349	1.350	1.349
(structure)	CC	1.398	—	1.406	1.390	1.390	1.397	1.384	1.389	1.388	1.390
(structure)	C_1C_2	1.531	—	1.499	1.467	1.465	1.581	1.479	1.477	1.476	1.478
	C_2C_3	1.482	—	1.382	1.373	1.371	1.356	1.352	1.353	1.353	1.354
	C_3C_4	1.480	—	1.426	1.409	1.406	1.422	1.407	1.410	1.409	1.410
$CH_3CO_2^-$	CC	1.527	1.519	1.553	1.528	1.543	1.631	1.576	1.554	1.553	1.547
	CO	1.365	1.263	1.263	1.266	1.257	1.263	1.250	1.234	1.234	1.238
CN^-	CN	1.170	—	1.179	1.179	1.172	1.162	1.166	1.161	1.161	1.162
(structure)	CC	1.440	—	1.401	1.395	1.394	1.419	1.400	1.412	1.412	1.412
	CN	1.158	—	1.169	1.170	1.170	1.162	1.150	1.145	1.145	1.146
NO_3^-	NO	1.365	1.242	1.235	1.225	1.239	1.315	1.283	1.226	1.226	1.227
CO_3^{2-}	CO	1.365	1.289	1.298	1.297	1.293	1.330	1.305	1.285	1.285	1.286
mean absolute error		0.057	0.015	0.019	0.017	0.015	0.032	0.014	0.012	0.012	0.011

46

cation/anion	bond	Hartree-Fock		MP2	density functional				expt.
		6-311G*	6-311+G**	6-31G*	SVWN/DN*	SVWN/DN**	pBP/DN*	pBP/DN**	
(structure)	CN	1.322	1.322	1.333	1.327	1.328	1.331	1.335	1.323
(structure)	CC	1.349	1.349	1.368	1.356	1.358	1.366	1.367	1.363-1.379
(structure)	CC	1.388	1.388	1.400	1.388	1.389	1.402	1.403	1.386-1.395
(structure)	C_1C_2	1.477	1.475	1.466	1.448	1.447	1.471	1.470	1.490
	C_2C_3	1.353	1.352	1.376	1.366	1.367	1.376	1.377	1.365
	C_3C_4	1.410	1.409	1.409	1.400	1.400	1.415	1.415	1.407
$CH_3CO_2^-$	CC	1.554	1.549	1.562	1.546	1.546	1.578	1.578	1.50-1.54
	CO	1.230	1.233	1.264	1.255	1.256	1.267	1.267	1.25-1.27
CN^-	CN	1.153	1.156	1.201	1.183	1.183	1.190	1.190	1.15
(structure)	CC	1.410	1.410	1.412	1.399	1.399	1.414	1.414	1.40-1.42
	CN	1.139	1.140	1.190	1.173	1.173	1.180	1.180	1.14-1.16
NO_3^-	NO	1.221	1.222	1.270	1.257	1.257	1.274	1.274	1.22-1.27
CO_3^{2-}	CO	1.282	1.282	1.315	1.307	1.307	1.323	1.323	1.29
mean absolute error		0.012	0.012	0.019	0.015	0.015	0.020	0.021	–

identical results, even for anions where diffuse functions might be expected to have some effect. MP2 and density functional models also provide acceptable descriptions of the geometries of charged systems, although (on the basis of mean absolute errors) they are not as good as those from Hartree-Fock models.

Comparisons between calculated and experimental geometries of hydrogen-bonded complexes are provided in **Table 3-5**. Here the gas-phase experimental data are subject to considerable uncertainty. Neither molecular mechanics nor semi-empirical molecular orbital models are very successful. Except for water dimer, all SYBYL hydrogen-bond lengths are much too long. MMFF94 mechanics is available only for water dimer, where the calculated OO bond distance is significantly shorter than the experimental value. This is deliberate. MMFF94 has been parameterized to properly reproduce the density of liquid water. The PM3 model provides a better overall account than either MNDO or AM1 (both of which sometimes assign incorrect equilibrium structures or lead to dissociation), although errors in bond lengths of two tenths of an Å or more occur.

Results from 6-31G* and larger-basis-set Hartree-Fock calculations are excellent, while those from STO-3G and 3-21G$^{(*)}$ calculations are less satisfactory. Interestingly, the addition of polarization functions to hydrogen (6-31G* to 6-31G**) appears to have little effect on geometries of hydrogen-bonded systems, while the addition of diffuse functions (6-31+G*) generally has the effect of increasing hydrogen-bond length. The MP2/6-31G*, pBP/DN* and pBP/DN** models also lead to good descriptions of hydrogen-bond lengths, but the SVWN/DN* and SVWN/DN** models are not as successful.

While supporting data have not been provided, Hartree-Fock models have not proven to be successful in dealing with the geometries of transition-metal inorganic and organometallic compounds. This is probably a direct consequence of ignoring electron correlation, the effects of which would be expected to be much greater for transition-metal systems (which often possess low-lying excited states) than for typical organic compounds. MP2 models would be expected to lead to acceptable descriptions although, because of the large size of typical metal containing systems, applications have been very limited. This is indeed an area where quantitative yet practical methods are needed.

Comparisons of calculated and experimental metal-carbon bond distances in transition-metal carbonyl compounds and transition-metal organometallics are provided in **Tables 3-6** and **3-7**, respectively. The PM3 model provides an acceptable account of the geometries of transition-metal compounds. Bond distances to carbon monoxide ligands are typically in error by only a few hundredths of an Å, including distances to bridging carbonyls. In addition, calculated metal-metal bond lengths in binuclear carbonyl compounds are quite close to experimental distances. Metal-ligand distances are also well reproduced. While not shown explicitly by the data in the table, the PM3 model correctly reproduces the overall shapes of all metal carbonyls and organometallics, including the binuclear carbonyl complexes.

Both local and non-local density functional models also provide a good description of bond distances in transition-metal carbonyls and organometallics. Bond lengths from SVWN calculations are usually shorter than experimental distances, the same trend generally noted for organic systems. Distances calculated using pBP models are usually longer than the corresponding SVWN bond lengths, and generally in better accord with the experimental data. Note that bond lengths involving bridging carbonyls (in binuclear complexes) are as well described as those for terminal carbonyls. While not shown explicitly by the data in the table, both density functional models correctly reproduce the overall shapes of all metal carbonyls and organometallics, including the binuclear carbonyl complexes.

Reaction Energies

Chemical reactions may be conveniently divided into one of several categories depending on the extent to which overall bonding is maintained (**Table 3-8**). The distinction is important as quantum chemical methods differ in the way they treat electron correlation. Hartree-Fock models completely ignore correlation, and would not be expected to properly describe the energetics of reactions in which

Table 3-5: Bond Lengths in Hydrogen-Bonded Complexes (Å)

hydrogen-bonded complex	bond	molecular mechanics		semi-empirical			Hartree-Fock				
		SYBYL	MMFF94	MNDO	AM1	PM3	STO-3G	3-21G$^{(*)}$	6-31G*	6-31G**	6-31+G*
(H₂O···H₂O)	OO	2.94	2.75	3.89[a]	3.06[a]	2.77	2.73	2.80	2.98	2.98	2.96
(HF···H₂O)	OF	3.20	—	3.95	2.41[a]	2.68	2.63	2.57	2.72	2.72	2.72
(HF···HF)	FF	3.04	—	3.92	2.91	2.68	2.57	2.60	2.72	2.72	2.79
(HCl···HF)	ClF	3.80	—	b	3.39	3.00	2.79	3.13	3.36	3.33	3.45
(HF···N≡C—H)	NF	3.07	—	3.98	3.43	2.76	3.03	2.81	2.92	2.90	2.92
mean absolute error		0.30	c	c	c	0.15	0.27	0.15	0.05	0.05	0.05

hydrogen-bonded complex	bond	Hartree-Fock		MP2	density functional				expt.
		6-311G*	6-311+G**	6-31G*	SVWN/DN*	SVWN/DN**	pBP/DN*	pBP/DN**	
(water dimer structure)	OO	2.91	3.00	2.91	2.72	2.73	2.88	2.88	2.98
(H–F···O(H)H structure)	OF	2.67	2.72	2.69	2.51	2.52	2.63	2.63	2.69
(H–F···F–H structure)	FF	2.73	2.83	2.64	2.56	2.56	2.70	2.68	2.79
(H–Cl···F–H structure)	ClF	3.35	3.45	3.24	3.09	3.05	3.28	3.22	3.37
(H–F···N≡C–H structure)	NF	2.90	2.90	2.87	2.63	2.62	2.76	2.73	2.80
mean absolute error		0.05	0.05	0.08	0.22	0.21	0.08	0.10	–

a) assigns incorrect (bifurcated) geometry.
b) dissociates or nearly dissociates.
c) insufficient data to obtain meaningful error.

Table 3-6: Bond Lengths in Transition-Metal Carbonyl Compounds (Å)

molecule	bond	semi-empirical PM3	density functional SVWN/DN*	pBP/DN*	expt.
$CrCO_6$	CrC	1.93	1.87	1.91	1.914
$MoCO_6$	MoC	2.07	2.05	2.09	2.063
Mn_2CO_{10}	MnMn	2.92	2.82	2.96	2.977
	MnC_{ax}	1.79	1.77	1.81	1.803
	MnC_{eq}	1.85	1.82	1.86	1.873
$FeCO_5$	FeC_{ax}	1.79	1.83	1.81	1.807
	FeC_{eq}	1.74	1.79	1.81	1.821
Fe_2CO_9	FeFe	2.60	2.45	2.53	2.523
	FeC_{term}	1.77	1.79	1.83	1.8
	FeC_{bridge}	1.99	1.97	2.02	1.9
$RuCO_5$	RuC_{ax}	1.93	1.98	1.97	1.950
	RuC_{eq}	1.90	1.99	1.99	1.969
Co_2CO_8	CoCo	2.56	2.48	2.56	2.52
	CoC_{term}	1.81	1.77	1.81	1.78
		1.82	1.78	1.82	1.80
	CoC_{bridge}	1.96	1.92	1.97	1.92
$NiCO_4$	NiC	1.80	1.79	1.83	1.82
mean absolute error		0.04	0.04	0.02	-

Table 3-7: Metal-Carbon Bond Lengths in Transition-Metal Organometallics (Å)

molecule	bond to	semi-empirical	density functional				expt.
		PM3	SVWN/DN*	SVWN/DN**	pBP/DN*	pBP/DN**	
Cp$_2$Ti...ethylene	ethylene	2.15	2.16	2.16	2.20	2.20	2.16
Cr...(benzene)$_2$	benzene	2.21	2.15	2.15	2.15	2.15	2.22
CO$_3$Cr..benzene	benzene	2.23	2.17	2.17	2.24	2.24	2.22
CO$_4$Cr...Dewar benzene	Dewar benzene C$_1$	2.20	2.29	2.29	2.30	2.30	2.33
	Dewar benzene C$_2$	2.77	2.80	2.80	2.80	2.80	2.80
CO$_5$Cr=C(Me)NH(Me)	=C	2.06	2.03	2.03	2.07	2.08	2.09
CO$_3$Fe...cyclobutadiene	cyclobutadiene	2.07	2.02	2.02	2.07	2.07	2.06
CO$_3$Fe...butadiene	butadiene C$_1$	2.05	2.07	2.08	2.13	2.13	2.14
	butadiene C$_2$	2.13	2.03	2.03	2.08	2.08	2.06
CO$_4$Fe...acetylene	acetylene	2.00	2.06	2.06	2.11	2.11	2.08
CO$_4$Fe...ethylene	ethylene	2.01	2.16	2.16	2.16	2.16	2.12
CO$_3$Co...allyl	allyl C$_1$	2.02	2.06	2.06	2.13	2.13	2.10
	allyl C$_2$	2.02	1.98	1.98	2.03	2.03	1.99
ClRh...(butadiene)$_2$	butadiene C$_1$	2.14	2.18	2.18	2.25	2.25	2.21
	butadiene C$_2$	2.20	2.17	2.17	2.22	2.22	2.15
Ni...(allyl)$_2$	allyl C$_1$	2.03	1.98	1.98	2.04	2.04	2.02
	allyl C$_2$	2.06	1.95	1.95	1.99	1.99	1.98
Cl$_2$Pd...cyclooctatetraene	cyclooctatetraene	2.15	2.19	2.19	2.27	2.27	2.21
mean absolute error		0.05	0.03	0.03	0.03	0.03	–

Table 3-8: Reaction Types

type of process	examples
no conservation of number of electron pairs	homolytic bond dissociation
conservation of number of electron pairs, but no conservation of number of bonds	heterolytic bond dissociation
conservation of number of bonds and number of nonbonded electron pairs, but no conservation of number of each kind of bond or number of each kind of nonbonded electron pair	hydrogenation, structural isomerism
conservation of number of each kind of bond and number of each type of nonbonded electron pair (*isodesmic* reactions)	bond separation, relative acidity and basicity comparisons

the bonding in reactants and products was markedly different. On the other hand, MP2 models and density functional models take partial account of correlation effects, and would be expected to perform better. Semi-empirical models are parameterized to directly reproduce experimental thermochemical data, and might be expected to perform equally well (or poorly) for all types of comparisons.

Processes in which not even the total number of electron pairs (bonds and nonbonded lone pairs) is conserved are at one extreme. **Homolytic bond dissociation** reactions, e.g.,

$H\text{-}F \rightarrow H\cdot + F\cdot$ *homolytic bond dissociation*

are an example. Comparisons of transition states and reactants (as required for the calculation of absolute activation energies) are also likely candidates for processes in which the total number of electron pairs is not conserved.

Less disruptive are reactions in which the total number of electron pairs is maintained, but a chemical bond is converted to a nonbonded lone pair or vice versa. **Heterolytic bond dissociation** reactions, e.g.,

$Na\text{-}F \rightarrow Na^+ + \ddot{F}^-$ *heterolytic bond dissociation*

and some structural isomerizations, e.g.,

$H_2C{=}O \rightarrow HC\ddot{O}H$ *structural isomerization*

are examples. The most important examples may again involve comparisons between transition states and reactants.

Reactions in which both the total number of bonds and the total number of nonbonded lone pairs are conserved are even less disruptive. Several examples are given below.

$H_2C{=}CH_2 + 2H_2 \rightarrow 2CH_4$ *hydrogenation*

$\overline{CH_2CH_2CH_2} \rightarrow CH_3CH{=}CH_2$ *structural isomerization*

$2CH_2{=}CH_2 \rightarrow H_3C\text{-}CH_3 + HC{\equiv}CH$ *disproportionation*

At the other extreme are reactions in which the number of each kind of formal chemical bond (and each kind of nonbonded lone pair) are conserved. These are *isodesmic* ("equal bond") reactions. Examples

55

include the processes below.

$$H_3C-C{\equiv}CH + CH_4 \rightarrow H_3C-CH_3 + HC{\equiv}CH \qquad \textit{bond separation}$$

$$(CH_3)_3NH^+ + NH_3 \rightarrow (CH_3)_3N + NH_4^+ \qquad \textit{proton transfer}$$

In addition, all regio and stereochemical comparisons are *isodesmic* reactions, as are conformation changes. Thus, *isodesmic* processes constitute a large class of reactions of considerable importance.

Comparisons of homolytic bond dissociation energies among the different models is provided in **Table 3-9**. Experimental data have been replaced by bond energies from the so-called G2 model.[1] This has been developed specifically for the purpose of producing thermochemical data on small molecules of uniform quality.

Homolytic bond dissociation energies obtained from the MNDO (MNDO/d), AM1 and PM3 semi-empirical models are not in good agreement with the "experimental data", somewhat surprising in view of the fact that the parameterizations for these models took explicit account of heats of formation of free radicals. None of the methods fares significantly better than the others, and none can be recommended for this purpose.

Hartree-Fock models also do not provide good accounts of homolytic bond dissociation energies. Errors are even larger than those resulting from semi-empirical models and are, for the most part, independent of the basis set. Note, that bond dissociation energies calculated from Hartree-Fock models are consistently smaller than experimental values. This follows from inadequate treatment of electron correlation and the fact that reactants and products differ by one electron pair. For example, the homolytic bond dissociation reaction for hydrogen molecule (not provided in the table) involves comparison of the energy of H_2 (too high in the limit of Hartree-Fock theory) with those of two hydrogen atoms (given exactly in the Hartree-Fock model). The result is that the bond energy is too small.

MP2/6-31G* and both pBP/DN* and pBP/DN** density functional models, which account for electron correlation, correctly reproduce homolytic bond dissociation energies. The performance of all three methods is similar, with errors typically in the range of 2-4 kcal/mol. On the other hand, local SVWN/DN* and SVWN/DN** models provide a very poor account, in all cases leading to values which are much too large.*

Hydrogenation reactions and structural isomer comparisons typify reactions which conserve only the total number of electron pairs, and do not conserve the numbers of individual bonds or the number of nonbonded lone pairs. It is to be expected that correlation effects will cancel in whole or in part, and that Hartree-Fock models might provide an acceptable account.

Data for hydrogenation reactions is provided in **Table 3-10**. All three semi-empirical models provide a very poor account. Surprisingly, the MNDO model is the best of the three, not only because it leads to the smallest mean absolute error, but also because this error is largely systematic in nature. AM1 and PM3 methods lead to significantly larger errors, a substantial component of which are random errors rather than systematic errors.

STO-3G and, to a lesser extent, 3-21G models are also not satisfactory for hydrogenation energy calculations. On the other hand, 6-31G* and larger-basis-set Hartree-Fock models perform well. While the energies of individual reactions show significant fluctuations with basis set (beyond 6-31G*), the mean absolute error computed for the entire set of compounds is largely unaffected.

The MP2/6-31G* model and both local and non-local density functional models perform well in the calculation of hydrogenation energies. The SVWN/DN* model is the least satisfactory and the pBP/DN** model is the most satisfactory.

Semi-empirical calculations provide a qualitatively correct but quantitatively poor description of the relative energies of structural isomers (**Table 3-11**). None of the three schemes is particularly better than any other, and none can be recommended for this purpose.

---

* The observation that Hartree-Fock models underestimate bond dissociation energies while local density functional models overestimate bond dissociation energies prompted the development of so-called hybrid density functional models, which combine components of each. For a discussion, see: A.D. Becke, *J. Chem. Phys.*, **98**, 5648 (1993).

Table 3-9: Homolytic Bond Dissociation Energies (kcal/mol)

bond dissociation reaction	semi-empirical			Hartree-Fock						
	MNDO	AM1	PM3	STO-3G	3-21G$^{(*)}$	6-31G*	6-31G**	6-31+G*	6-311G*	6-311+G**
$CH_3\text{-}CH_3 \rightarrow 2CH_3^{\cdot}$	69	77	74	95	68	69	69	67	68	66
$CH_3\text{-}NH_2 \rightarrow CH_3^{\cdot} + NH_2^{\cdot}$	69	75	68	73	59	58	58	58	58	57
$CH_3\text{-}OH \rightarrow CH_3^{\cdot} + OH^{\cdot}$	82	88	83	67	53	58	59	58	59	58
$CH_3\text{-}F \rightarrow CH_3^{\cdot} + F^{\cdot}$	104	110	101	66	72	69	69	70	68	69
$CH_3\text{-}SiH_3 \rightarrow CH_3^{\cdot} + SiH_3^{\cdot}$	78	66	74	98	72	67	67	66	67	66
$CH_3\text{-}PH_2 \rightarrow CH_3^{\cdot} + PH_2^{\cdot}$	64	65	67	74	52	49	48	48	49	47
$CH_3\text{-}SH \rightarrow CH_3^{\cdot} + SH^{\cdot}$	63	74	71	68	48	48	48	47	48	46
$CH_3\text{-}Cl \rightarrow CH_3^{\cdot} + Cl^{\cdot}$	72	78	72	65	51	54	54	53	54	53
$NH_2\text{-}NH_2 \rightarrow 2NH_2^{\cdot}$	59	62	50	44	37	34	34	34	36	33
$HO\text{-}OH \rightarrow 2OH^{\cdot}$	39	37	46	22	3	0	0	-1	1	2
$F\text{-}F \rightarrow 2F^{\cdot}$	30	60	59	5	-29	-33	-33	-37	-39	-39
$SiH_3\text{-}SiH_3 \rightarrow 2SiH_3^{\cdot}$	65	33	66	96	60	58	58	58	58	57
$PH_2\text{-}PH_2 \rightarrow 2PH_2^{\cdot}$	62	62	61	51	35	33	33	33	34	32
$HS\text{-}SH \rightarrow 2SH^{\cdot}$	67	70	66	44	30	29	28	28	28	28
$Cl\text{-}Cl \rightarrow 2Cl^{\cdot}$	59	72	70	19	10	11	11	11	10	12
mean absolute error	9	10	10	19	33	33	33	34	33	34

hydrogenation reaction	MP2 6-31G*	density functional				G2[a]
		SVWN/DN*	SVWN/DN**	pBP/DN*	pBP/DN**	
CH_3-$CH_3 \rightarrow 2CH_3^{\bullet}$	99	117	116	95	93	88
CH_3-$NH_2 \rightarrow CH_3^{\bullet} + NH_2^{\bullet}$	92	115	114	90	89	83
CH_3-$OH \rightarrow CH_3^{\bullet} + OH^{\bullet}$	98	123	122	97	97	92
CH_3-$F \rightarrow CH_3^{\bullet} + F^{\bullet}$	113	142	141	116	115	111
CH_3-$SiH_3 \rightarrow CH_3^{\bullet} + SiH_3^{\bullet}$	90	105	104	88	86	–
CH_3-$PH_2 \rightarrow CH_3^{\bullet} + PH_2^{\bullet}$	74	93	92	74	72	70
CH_3-$SH \rightarrow CH_3^{\bullet} + SH^{\bullet}$	77	96	96	79	78	73
CH_3-$Cl \rightarrow CH_3^{\bullet} + Cl^{\bullet}$	90	104	104	87	86	83
NH_2-$NH_2 \rightarrow 2NH_2^{\bullet}$	74	101	100	74	73	64
HO-$OH \rightarrow 2OH^{\bullet}$	56	86	86	60	60	49
F-$F \rightarrow 2F^{\bullet}$	38	75	74	49	49	37
SiH_3-$SiH_3 \rightarrow 2SiH_3^{\bullet}$	73	86	85	73	72	76
PH_2-$PH_2 \rightarrow 2PH_2^{\bullet}$	53	74	73	57	57	56
HS-$SH \rightarrow 2SH^{\bullet}$	55	81	81	67	67	61
Cl-$Cl \rightarrow 2Cl^{\bullet}$	54	72	72	59	59	56
mean absolute error	5	26	26	6	5	–

a) Derived from data in reference 1.

Table 3-10: Energies of Hydrogenation Reactions (kcal/mol)

hydrogenation reaction	semi-empirical			Hartree-Fock						
	MNDO	AM1	PM3	STO-3G	3-21G	6-31G*	6-31G**	6-31+G*	6-311G*	6-311+G*
$CH_3-CH_3 + H_2 \rightarrow 2CH_4$	-5	5	6	-19	-25	-22	-21	-22	-22	-21
$CH_3-NH_2 + H_2 \rightarrow CH_4 + NH_3$	-11	-3	3	-20	-30	-27	-28	-28	-27	-28
$CH_3-OH + H_2 \rightarrow CH_4 + H_2O$	-16	-6	1	-16	-28	-27	-30	-29	-27	-31
$CH_3-F + H_2 \rightarrow CH_4 + HF$	-11	-17	-9	-8	-22	-23	-27	-25	-23	-29
$F-F + H_2 \rightarrow 2HF$	-128	-121	-90	-29	-98	-126	-134	-141	-131	-149
$H_2C=CH_2 + 2H_2 \rightarrow 2CH_4$	-41	-24	-16	-91	-71	-66	-64	-64	-64	-61
$HC\equiv CH + 3H_2 \rightarrow 2CH_4$	-84	-57	-37	-154	-124	-121	-118	-118	-117	-112
mean absolute error	15	25	37	33	12	6	4	5	5	4

hydrogenation reaction	MP2	density functional				expt.
	6-31G*	SVWN/DN*	SVWN/DN**	pBP/DN*	pBP/DN**	
$CH_3-CH_3 + H_2 \rightarrow 2CH_4$	-16	-16	-18	-18	-19	-19
$CH_3-NH_2 + H_2 \rightarrow CH_4 + NH_3$	-23	-23	-25	-24	-27	-26
$CH_3-OH + H_2 \rightarrow CH_4 + H_2O$	-25	-26	-29	-26	-30	-30
$CH_3-F + H_2 \rightarrow CH_4 + HF$	-21	-26	-29	-25	-28	-29
$F-F + H_2 \rightarrow 2HF$	-116	-126	-133	-119	-126	-133
$H_2C=CH_2 + 2H_2 \rightarrow 2CH_4$	-58	-66	-66	-57	-58	-57
$HC\equiv CH + 3H_2 \rightarrow 2CH_4$	-104	-126	-127	-107	-109	-105
mean absolute error	5	7	5	4	2	–

The STO-3G model and, to a lesser extent the 3-21G model, are also unreliable for structural isomer comparisons and cannot be recommended for this purpose. On the other hand, Hartree-Fock calculations using 6-31G* and larger basis sets generally yield results which are quite close to experimental values. As with hydrogenation energies, there seems to be little benefit to basis sets larger than 6-31G* for structural isomer comparisons at the Hartree-Fock level.

MP2 and density functional models also provide a good account of relative isomer energies, although not markedly better than that provided by the Hartree-Fock models using the 6-31G* and larger basis sets. The most unusual result involves comparison of propyne and allene using density functional models. In disagreement with experiment, both SVWN and pBP models show allene to be the more stable than propyne. This behavior has been seen with other density functional models, and no explanation for it has been advanced. The MP2/6-31G* model properly orders isomer stability.

Isodesmic processes are represented by bond separation reactions, by reactions comparing acidities of carbon acids relative to propene and basicities of nitrogen compounds relative to ammonia. It is reasonable to expect that energetic comparisons such as these will be much better accommodated using models which do not account for electron correlation, i.e., Hartree-Fock models, than the types of comparisons discussed until now. The most interesting question is perhaps whether these simple models provide as good an account of energetics as more costly correlated schemes.

Energies of bond separation reactions obtained from the various calculations appear in **Table 3-12**. Semi-empirical models are not satisfactory. The MNDO and PM3 models provide a better account than AM1, but reaction energies are typically in error by 10 kcal/mol or more. On the other hand, Hartree-Fock models usually provide good descriptions. The exception involves reactions with small strained rings, where the STO-3G model and, to a lesser extent, the 3-21G model fare poorly. Results from Hartree-Fock 6-31G* calculations typically deviate from experimental bond separation energies by 1-2 kcal/mol, and at most by 6 kcal/mol. Larger-basis-

Table 3-11: Relative Energies of Structural Isomers (kcal/mol)

formula	isomer	semi-empirical			Hartree-Fock						
		MNDO	AM1	PM3	STO-3G	3-21G	6-31G*	6-31G**	6-31+G*	6-311G*	6-311+G**
C_2H_3N	(relative to acetonitrile)										
	methyl isocyanide	41	31	31	24	21	21	21	19	20	20
C_2H_4O	(relative to acetaldehyde)										
	oxirane	27	33	36	11	34	31	30	31	32	32
C_3H_4	(relative to propyne)										
	allene	3	3	7	17	3	2	2	2	3	2
	cyclopropene	27	31	28	30	40	26	26	27	28	28
C_3H_6	(relative to propene)										
	cyclopropane	6	11	10	-4	14	8	8	9	10	10
C_3H_6O	(relative to acetone)										
	propanal	2	1	4	6	6	6	6	7	6	7
	allyl alcohol	12	10	20	32	21	28	25	26	27	22
	methyl vinyl ether	23	22	28	25	20	29	29	28	29	28
	oxetane	12	24	27	2	30	33	33	34	34	34
mean absolute error		7	7	5	10	5	2	2	3	3	2

formula	isomer	MP2 6-31G*	density functional				expt.
			SVWN/DN*	SVWN/DN**	pBP/DN*	pBP/DN**	
C$_2$H$_3$N	(relative to acetonitrile)						
	methyl isocyanide	29	25	25	25	25	21
C$_2$H$_4$O	(relative to acetaldehyde)						
	oxirane	27	23	23	26	26	26
C$_3$H$_4$	(relative to propyne)						
	allene	5	-3	-3	-3	-3	2
	cyclopropene	23	18	17	21	21	22
C$_3$H$_6$	(relative to propene)						
	cyclopropane	4	2	3	7	7	7
C$_3$H$_6$O	(relative to acetone)						
	propanal	6	7	7	7	7	7
	allyl alcohol	29	25	22	26	22	22
	methyl vinyl ether	30	24	26	26	25	26
	oxetane	33	28	27	32	32	31
mean absolute error		3	3	3	2	1	–

Table 3-12: Energies of Bond Separation Reactions (kcal/mol)

bond separation reaction	semi-empirical			STO-3G	3-21G	Hartree-Fock				
	MNDO	AM1	PM3			6-31G*	6-31G**	6-31+G*	6-311G*	6-311+G**
$CH_3CH_2NH_2 + CH_4 \rightarrow CH_3CH_3 + CH_3NH_2$	-2	-1	2	2	3	3	3	3	3	3
$CH_3CH_2OH + CH_4 \rightarrow CH_3CH_3 + CH_3OH$	-2	-3	0	3	5	4	4	4	5	4
$CH_3CH=CH_2 + CH_4 \rightarrow CH_3CH_3 + CH_2=CH_2$	3	1	5	5	4	4	4	4	4	4
$CH_3CHO + CH_4 \rightarrow CH_3CH_3 + H_2CO$	2	0	5	8	10	10	10	10	10	10
$NH_2CHO + CH_4 \rightarrow CH_3NH_2 + H_2CO$	11	15	14	20	37	31	32	31	31	30
△ $+ 3CH_4 \rightarrow 3CH_3CH_3$	-35	-44	-32	-45	-31	-26	-25	-25	-27	-25
(NH)△ $+ 2CH_4 + NH_3 \rightarrow CH_3CH_3 + 2CH_3NH_2$	-30	-40	-31	-40	-33	-22	-21	-22	-22	-21
(O)△ $+ 2CH_4 + H_2O \rightarrow CH_3CH_3 + 2CH_3OH$	-34	-46	-34	-35	-31	-20	-19	-19	-20	-19
mean absolute error	11	15	9	10	7	2	2	2	2	2

bond separation reaction	MP2 6-31G*	density functional SVWN/DN*	SVWN/DN**	pBP/DN*	pBP/DN**	expt.
$CH_3CH_2NH_2 + CH_4 \rightarrow CH_3CH_3 + CH_3NH_2$	4	4	5	3	3	3
$CH_3CH_2OH + CH_4 \rightarrow CH_3CH_3 + CH_3OH$	5	6	6	4	5	5
$CH_3CH=CH_2 + CH_4 \rightarrow CH_3CH_3 + CH_2=CH_2$	5	6	6	5	5	5
$CH_3CHO + CH_4 \rightarrow CH_3CH_3 + H_2CO$	11	13	13	11	11	11
$NH_2CHO + CH_4 \rightarrow CH_3NH_2 + H_2CO$	33	38	39	34	34	30
△ $+ 3CH_4 \rightarrow 3CH_3CH_3$	-24	-30	-28	-23	-21	-22
△(NH) $+ 2CH_4 + NH_3 \rightarrow CH_3CH_3 + 2CH_3NH_2$	-18	-25	-23	-17	-16	-17
△(O) $+ 2CH_4 + H_2O \rightarrow CH_3CH_3 + 2CH_3OH$	-13	-20	-19	-13	-12	-14
mean absolute error	1	4	4	1	1	–

set Hartree-Fock models provide similar quality results, and their use (in lieu of 6-31G*) is difficult to justify for this purpose.

The performance of MP2 and density functional models for bond separation reactions is very similar to that for Hartree-Fock models. pBP models are uniformly better than SVWN models for both DN* and DN** basis sets. There appears to be little benefit to explicitly treating electron correlation for reactions of this type, although on the basis of cost alone the advantage may go to the pBP/DN* model.

Calculated acidities of carbon acids, relative to the acidity of propene, are compared to experimental relative acidities in **Table 3-13**. While all models are able to distinguish between very weak carbon acids, e.g., methane, moderately strong acids, e.g., toluene, and very strong acids, e.g., nitromethane, none of the simple models is able to provide a quantitative account of relative acidities. In particular, results from both semi-empirical models and small-basis-set Hartree-Fock models are unacceptable. On the other hand, Hartree-Fock models with the 6-31G* basis set or larger, the MP2/6-31G* model and both SVWN and pBP models provide a reasonably quantitative account of relative carbon acidities. Note that the inclusion of diffuse functions (in Hartree-Fock models) does have a noticeable (and beneficial) effect on calculated relative acidities.

Calculated basicities of nitrogen compounds, relative to the basicity of ammonia, are compared to experimental relative basicities in **Table 3-14**. As with all other energetic comparisons, semi-empirical models perform poorly. They are not even able to properly distinguish the relative strengths of primary, secondary and tertiary amines.

Hartree-Fock models, STO-3G included, properly assign relative nitrogen basicities. The worst performance is for the 3-21G model. This is probably a direct consequence of the known deficiency of Hartree-Fock 3-21G calculations to properly describe the geometry about nitrogen in amines. Basis set extensions beyond 6-31G* lead to no significant improvements in relative basicity results, and it is difficult to justify their use for this purpose.

Correlated models also perform well for relative basicity calculations.

Table 3-13: Acidities of Carbon Acids Relative to Propene (kcal/mol)[a]

carbon acid XCH₃	semi-empirical			Hartree-Fock						
	MNDO	AM1	PM3	STO-3G	3-21G	6-31G*	6-31G**	6-31+G*	6-311G*	6-311+G**
methane	-48	-46	-46	-45	-37	-32	-32	-26	-28	-26
toluene	16	15	15	18	9	10	10	6	9	6
1,1,1-trifluoroethane	8	3	8	1	13	8	7	6	8	5
acetonitrile	8	9	13	18	21	23	23	19	21	19
acetaldehyde	14	16	14	12	28	28	28	26	26	25
nitromethane	39	40	46	40	54	46	46	40	41	39
mean absolute error	10	10	10	10	8	7	7	5	5	4

carbon acid XCH₃	MP2	density functional				expt.
	6-31G*	SVWN/DN*	SVWN/DN**	pBP/DN*	pBP/DN**	
methane	-37	-38	-39	-36	-37	-26
toluene	12	12	11	11	11	12
1,1,1-trifluoroethane	9	7	7	11	10	16±3
acetonitrile	20	19	19	19	18	18
acetaldehyde	29	27	26	26	26	24
nitromethane	39	36	35	36	35	32
mean absolute error	5	5	5	4	4	–

a) Energies (enthalpies) of reactions: $XCH_2^- + CH_3CH=CH_2 \rightarrow XCH_3 + CH_2CHCH_2^-$, where XCH_3 is the carbon acid.

Table 3-14: Basicities of Nitrogen Bases Relative to Ammonia (kcal/mol)[a]

nitrogen base B	semi-empirical			Hartree-Fock						
	MNDO	AM1	PM3	STO-3G	3-21G	6-31G*	6-31G**	6-31+G*	6-311G*	6-311+G**
nitrogen	-65	-65	-70	-118	-101	-99	-99	-97	-100	-96
acetonitrile	-18	-19	-19	-38	-28	-23	-23	-22	-25	-21
methyleneimine	4	0	-8	-1	4	5	6	6	4	6
aniline	5	3	7	8	1	8	6	6	6	6
methylamine	2	2	-2	9	17	11	11	11	11	12
aziridine	5	3	-6	9	13	14	15	16	14	16
ethylamine	3	4	0	13	17	14	14	15	14	15
pyridine	12	8	0	18	21	18	18	18	16	19
dimethylamine	2	3	-4	15	14	18	18	19	17	19
trimethylamine	1	4	-6	20	10	22	22	23	21	24
quinuclidine	10	12	3	31	31	33	33	35	33	35
mean absolute error	10	10	14	5	6	4	4	4	3	4

| | MP2 | density functional | | | | |
nitrogen base B	6-31G*	SVWN/DN*	SVWN/DN**	pBP/DN*	pBP/DN**	expt.
nitrogen	-98	-94	-89	-94	-89	-94
acetonitrile	-29	-23	-18	-24	-20	-17
methyleneimine	-1	-1	1	-1	1	-3
aniline	5	1	2	4	4	7
methylamine	10	10	10	11	11	9
aziridine	9	11	10	12	11	10
ethylamine	13	12	13	13	14	12
pyridine	13	13	15	14	16	15
dimethylamine	16	13	16	15	18	16
trimethylamine	19	13	19	16	22	19
quinuclidine	–	24	31	28	33	30
mean absolute error	3	3	2	2	3	–

a) Energies (enthalpies) for reactions: $BH^+ + NH_3 \rightarrow B + NH_4^+$, where B is the nitrogen base.

There does not appear to be any advantage of the MP2 model over either local or non-local density functional models, or of any of the correlated models over the Hartree-Fock 6-31G* model, although on the basis of cost alone the advantage may go to pBP models.

Conformational Energy Differences

More than any other factors, single-bond conformation and ring conformation dictate overall molecular size and shape. Thus, proper assignment of ground-state conformation is a very important task for calculation. Conformation changes are examples of *isodesmic* reactions and, therefore, would be expected to be well described using simple models (but perhaps not semi-empirical models). However, conformational energy differences are typically very small (on the order of 1-5 kcal/mol), and even small errors might lead to incorrect assignment of ground-state conformer. An added concern is that numerical errors associated with density functional calculations may "swamp" small conformational energy differences leading to meaningless results for some systems.

A comparison of calculated and measured conformational energy differences for acyclic systems is provided in **Table 3-15**. The experimental data for some systems are subject to large uncertainties, and too much weight cannot be placed on quantitative comparisons. SYBYL molecular mechanics is completely unsatisfactory for describing conformational energy differences in acyclic systems, and should not be employed for this purpose. On the other hand, the MMFF94 mechanics model provides a good account of all systems examined.[*] In fact, the performance of MMFF94 is significantly better than any of the semi-empirical models, and in the same league as the best Hartree-Fock and correlated models (see below).

MNDO (MNDO/d), AM1 and PM3 models are unsatisfactory for assignment of ground-state conformer and calculation of conformational energy differences in acyclic systems. This could have been anticipated given the poor performance of semi-empirical models

---

[*] It should be noted that many of the molecules used in the conformation energy comparisons presented here have been drawn from the "training set" used to determine MMFF94 parameters.

for other *isodesmic* processes (see **Tables 3-12** to **3-14**). In many cases, the models either yield the wrong ground-state conformer or produce energy differences which are far smaller than experimental values. Semi-empirical models should not be employed for conformational assignments.

Except for systems where the difference in energy between conformers is very small, even the STO-3G model properly assigns ground-state conformation. However, conformational energy differences from STO-3G calculations show large errors in some cases, and results from 3-21G$^{(*)}$ calculations are generally even worse. The simplest Hartree-Fock model to provide a reliable (and for the most part quantitative) account of conformational energy differences is 6-31G*. Larger-basis-set Hartree-Fock models yield only marginal improvements, and there seems little justification in their use in lieu of the 6-31G* model.

In general, the MP2/6-31G* model also correctly assigns the known ground-state conformer in acyclic systems, as well as provides a reasonable account of energy differences. Unfortunately, calculations at this level are impractical for any but the smallest systems. On the other hand, density functional models are practical. Both local and especially non-local pBP models perform very well in their assignment of ground-state conformation, and calculated energy differences are comparable to those obtained at the MP2/6-31G* level. To some extent this allays concerns that numerical errors in density functional models may make them unsuitable for conformation energy calculations.

Similar comments apply to cyclic systems (**Table 3-16**). SYBYL molecular mechanics is completely unsatisfactory for establishing relative conformer stabilities, while MMFF94 appears to be quite well suited for this purpose. The only unsatisfactory case for MMFF94 is 2-chlorotetrahydropyran, where the noted preference for an axial arrangement (usually attributed to the anomeric effect) is not reproduced. Caution should be exercised in the application of MMFF94 to carbohydrates where the anomeric effect may lead to significant conformational preferences.

Table 3-15: Conformational Energy Differences in Acyclic Molecules (kcal/mol)

molecule	low-energy/ high energy conformer	molecular mechanics		semi-empirical			Hartree Fock				
		SYBYL	MMFF94	MNDO	AM1	PM3	STO-3G	3-21G$^{(*)}$	6-31G*	6-31G**	6-31+G*
n-butane	*trans/gauche*	0.6	0.8	0.6	0.7	0.5	0.9	0.8	0.9	0.9	1.0
1-butene	*skew/cis*	1.0	0.3	1.3	0.6	1.0	0.8	0.8	0.7	0.7	0.8
1,3-butadiene	*trans/gauche*	1.0	2.5	0.3	0.8	1.7	1.8	3.5	3.0	3.0	3.1
acrolein	*trans/cis*	0.0	2.0	-0.4	-0.2	0.4	0.5	0.0	1.7	1.6	2.1
N-methylformamide	*trans/cis*	0.3	1.3	0.4	-0.5	-1.5	0.3	1.5	1.1	1.1	1.2
N-methylacetamide	*trans/cis*	-1.8	2.6	-1.7	0.4	-0.5	2.4	3.9	2.8	3.1	3.2
formic acid	*cis/trans*	0.9	4.9	3.7	7.4	4.3	4.4	7.2	6.1	6.0	5.8
methyl formate	*cis/trans*	-0.3	5.3	2.9	5.6	1.9	3.9	7.0	6.3	6.2	6.2
methyl acetate	*cis/trans*	2.3	8.3	5.2	5.3	1.2	7.2	9.7	9.4	9.5	9.4
propanal	*cis/skew*	-0.1	0.5	-0.5	-0.7	-0.7	0.1	1.7	1.1	1.2	0.7
1,2-difluoroethane	*gauche/anti*	0.0	0.6	0.3	-0.5	1.4	0.3	-0.9	-0.5	-0.4	-0.2
1,2-dichloroethane	*anti/gauche*	0.0	1.2	1.1	0.8	0.6	1.4	1.8	1.9	1.8	2.0
ethanol	*anti/gauche*	-0.1	0.2	0.4	-1.6	-1.9	-0.2	-0.2	0.1	0.1	0.3
methyl ethyl ether	*anti/gauche*	0.5	1.5	0.9	-0.4	-1.0	1.3	1.0	1.7	1.7	1.8
methyl vinyl ether	*cis/skew*	-3.1	2.2	-0.6	2.1	1.7	0.9	3.3	2.0	1.9	1.9
mean absolute error		2.3	0.3	1.4	1.6	1.8	0.6	1.2	0.7	0.7	0.7

molecule	low-energy/ high energy conformer	Hartree-Fock		MP2	density functional				expt.
		6-311G*	6-311+G**	6-31G*	SVWN/DN*	SVWN/DN**	pBP/DN*	pBP/DN**	
n-butane	*trans/gauche*	1.0	1.0	0.7	0.7	1.3	1.2	1.2	0.77
1-butene	*skew/cis*	0.7	0.7	0.5	-1.0	0.3	0.5	0.4	0.2
1,3-butadiene	*trans/gauche*	3.2	3.2	2.6	3.8	4.2	4.0	3.9	1.7>2,2.5
acrolein	*trans/cis*	1.7	2.2	1.5	2.3	2.1	2.2	2.2	2.0,2.06
N-methylformamide	*trans/cis*	1.1	1.3	1.3	1.4	0.3	1.0	1.0	1.45
N-methylacetamide	*trans/cis*	3.0	3.4	2.7	2.1	2.4	2.3	2.3	2.3,2.8
formic acid	*cis/trans*	6.2	5.4	5.9	4.8	4.2	4.6	4.6	3.90
methyl formate	*cis/trans*	6.0	6.0	6.4	5.7	4.8	5.0	4.8	3.85,4.75
methyl acetate	*cis/trans*	9.4	9.4	8.9	6.4	7.7	7.4	7.4	8.5
propanal	*cis/skew*	1.1	0.8	1.4	1.6	1.2	0.9	0.9	0.67,0.95
1,2-difluoroethane	*gauche/anti*	-0.2	0.2	0.2	0.9	0.8	0.2	0.3	0.8
1,2-dichloroethane	*anti/gauche*	1.9	1.9	1.5	1.7	2.1	2.3	2.1	1.16
ethanol	*anti/gauche*	0.3	0.3	-0.1	0.3	-0.3	0.2	0.2	0.12,0.4
methyl ethyl ether	*anti/gauche*	1.9	1.8	1.4	1.0	1.8	1.3	1.5	1.5
methyl vinyl ether	*cis/skew*	2.0	1.8	2.8	3.2	1.7	1.7	1.8	1.7
mean absolute error		0.6	0.6	0.6	0.8	0.5	0.5	0.5	–

Table 3-16: Conformational Energy Differences in Cyclic Systems (kcal/mol)

molecule	low-energy/ high energy conformer	molecular mechanics		semi-empirical			Hartree Fock				
		SYBYL	MMFF94	MNDO	AM1	PM3	STO-3G	3-21G(*)	6-31G(*)	6-31G**	6-31+G*
cyclohexane	chair/twist boat	7.7	5.9	2.4	3.2	4.1	6.1	6.6	6.8	6.8	6.7
methylcyclohexane	equatorial/axial	1.0	1.4	1.0	1.4	1.1	1.8	1.9	2.3	2.3	2.4
tert-butylcyclohexane	equatorial/axial	7.4	6.3	3.9	5.1	1.1	6.4	6.6	6.3	6.1	6.3
piperidine	equatorial/axial	0.0	0.9	0.5	-2.7	-2.2	-0.4	0.3	0.8	0.8	0.9
N-methylpiperidine	equatorial/axial	0.5	3.3	1.3	-1.4	-1.3	2.0	2.0	3.6	3.6	4.0
2-chlorotetrahydropyran	axial/equatorial	-0.1	-0.1	1.8	3.6	3.1	3.2	3.6	2.5	2.5	2.4
mean absolute error		1.7	0.7	1.2	2.1	2.5	0.8	0.8	0.7	0.7	0.8

molecule	low-energy/high energy conformer	Hartree-Fock		MP2	density functional				expt.
		6-311G*	6-311+G**	6-31G*	SVWN/DN*	SVWN/DN**	pBP/DN*	pBP/DN**	
cyclohexane	*chair/twist boat*	6.8	6.9	6.6	6.9	6.0	7.0	6.8	5.5
methylcyclohexane	*equatorial/axial*	2.4	2.3	1.9	1.8	2.6	1.9	1.8	1.8
tert-butylcyclohexane	*equatorial/axial*	6.1	6.2	–	5.2	5.7	5.5	5.0	5.4
piperidine	*equatorial/axial*	1.1	0.9	0.6	0.6	0.6	0.5	0.2	0.4
N-methylpiperidine	*equatorial/axial*	4.0	3.9	3.3	4.2	3.8	3.9	3.5	3.15
2-chlorotetrahydropyran	*axial/equatorial*	2.3	2.7	2.8	4.2	4.5	4.2	4.6	1.8
mean absolute error		0.8	0.8	0.5	0.9	0.9	0.8	0.8	–

As with acyclic systems, semi-empirical MNDO (MNDO/d) AM1 and PM3 models do not provide a good account of the ground-state conformation and conformational energy differences in cyclic systems. While the models usually yield reasonable results for hydrocarbons, results for other systems are not acceptable. The performance of the PM3 model with regard to the equatorial/axial energy difference in *tert*-butylcyclohexane warrants additional comment. PM3 assigns the correct (equatorial) ground-state conformation for the molecule, but yields an energy difference to the axial form of only about 1 kcal/mol. This is far smaller than the experimental equatorial/axial separation of 5.5 kcal/mol, and the same as the calculated PM3 difference in methylcyclohexane. The problem can be traced to a tendency of nonbonded atoms (especially hydrogens) to attract each other in the PM3 model.*

Except for piperidine, the STO-3G model properly assigns the ground-state conformer for all systems. Energy differences are generally (but not always) lower than experimental separations. The 3-21G⁽*⁾, 6-31G* and larger-basis-set Hartree-Fock models properly account for the known ground-state conformation of all compounds, and generally yield energy differences in reasonable accord with the experimental data. As was the case with acyclic systems, Hartree-Fock models with basis sets larger than 6-31G* lead to only marginal improvements and their use is difficult to justify.

The MP2/6-31G* model properly assigns the ground-state conformation in all cases. The overall quality of the data (insofar as energy differences are concerned) is, however, no better than that from the corresponding Hartree-Fock 6-31G* model. There appears to be little justification for using MP2 models over the corresponding Hartree-Fock models for assigning ground-state conformers and establishing conformational energy differences.

Errors from density functional calculations (both local and non local) are larger than those from MP2 calculations, and comparable to those

---

* This problem has been addressed in a modification of the PM3 model available in SPARTAN, which introduces a hydrogen-hydrogen repulsive term. With this modification, the equatorial/axial energy difference in *tert*-butylcyclohexane increases to 4.8 kcal/mol.

from Hartree-Fock calculations. Cost considerations may justify use of pBP calculations in lieu of Hartree-Fock and MP2 calculations for evaluation of conformational energy differences in larger systems. As with acyclic systems discussed previously, the results are quite good, the only important exception being an overestimation of the energy difference between axial and equatorial conformers of 2-chlorotetrahydropyran.

Transition-State Geometries and Activation Energies

Quantum chemical calculations are not limited to the description of the structures and properties of stable molecules, that is, molecules which can be observed and characterized experimentally. They may also be applied to molecules which are very reactive ("reactive intermediates") and, most interesting of all, molecules which are not minima on the overall potential energy surface, but rather correspond to species which connect energy minima ("transition states" or "transition structures"). Here there are (and there can be) no experimental structure data, because transition states do not exist in the sense that they can be observed let alone characterized. However, the energies of transition states, relative to energies of reactants, may be inferred from experimental reaction rates.

At the present time, molecular mechanics calculations are limited to the description (of equilibrium geometries and conformations) of stable molecules, i.e., where parameters are available. It is quite likely, however, that future molecular mechanics models will be developed to deal with transition states. Here, calculations and not experiments will need to be the source of data for parameterization.

The complete lack of experimental data on transition-state geometries greatly complicates assessment of the performance of different models. The only recourse is to assume that some particular (high level) model yields "reasonable" geometries, and to compare the results of the other models with this "standard". Unfortunately, determination of transition-state geometries is still a difficult matter, and the "best" techniques are not yet practical for any but the simplest systems. As a compromise, the MP2/ 6-31G* model has been selected as a standard in the comparisons which follow. MP2/6-31G* is simple enough for widespread use (with simple molecules), and while supporting data have not been provided, generally appears to provide a satisfactory account of transition-state geometries (in comparison to the results from even higher-level models) and absolute activation energies (in comparison with experiment).

Key bond distances in transition-states for isomerization of methylisocyanide to acetonitrile, Diels-Alder cycloaddition of *cis*-1,3-butadiene and ethene, and pyrolysis of ethyl formate, leading to formic acid and ethene, obtained from semi-empirical calculations, Hartree-Fock calculations and SVWN and pBP density functional calculations, are compared to MP2/6-31G* results in **Table 3-17**. The variations in bond distance noted from one level of calculation to another are much larger than those found in analogous treatments of equilibrium geometries (see **Tables 3-1** and **3-2**). This is not unexpected. Transition states represent a "compromise situation" where some bonds are being broken and others formed, and the potential energy surface around the transition state would be expected to be "flat".

AM1 and PM3 models furnish a credible account of transition-state structures for these reactions, although there are some significant differences with MP2/6-31G* calculations. For one, both semi-empirical models show a much "tighter" transition-state for Diels-Alder cycloaddition (Hartree-Fock models also show a somewhat tighter transition structure for this reaction; see below). Also, the PM3 model depicts a much later transition state for the ethyl formate pyrolysis reaction. The MNDO model is not as successful. The mean absolute deviation from MP2/6-31G* in calculated bond distances is nearly twice as large as that resulting from AM1 and PM3 calculations, and the transition state for the Diels-Alder cycloaddition severely distorts to a diradical like structure, i.e., one bond is fully formed and the other is unformed.

With the possible exception of STO-3G, all Hartree-Fock models yield structures which are markedly similar. The STO-3G model provides a very similar account to the other models for the methylisocyanide rearrangement and for the Diels-Alder cycloaddition, but quite a different description of the ethyl formate pyrolysis reaction. The 6-31G* model and Hartree-Fock models with larger basis sets yield very similar transition-state geometries. There are differences in details, but mean absolute deviations from MP2/6-31G* structures are nearly identical.

To some extent, transition-state structures from the pBP models are similar to those from MP2/6-31G*, while those from the SVWN models are similar to those from the Hartree-Fock 6-31G* model. This parallels behavior already noted for equilibrium geometries (see **Tables 3-1** and **3-2**).

There are limited experimental data available for activation energies for simple organic reactions and, even where data are available, comparisons with calculated activation energies need to be made with some caution. For one, the calculations need to assume a "mechanism"; it is possible that this does not correspond to what actually occurs. Secondly, interpretation of the experimental data is based on the assumption that all reactants actually proceed over a unique transition state. Because of the incompleteness of the experimental data and the uncertainty in its interpretation, a "standard" has also been invoked. This again is the MP2/6-31G* model. For some of the larger systems, the MP2/6-31G* model is prohibitive for transition-state determinations, and Hartree-Fock 6-31G* reactant and transition-state geometries are used instead (for single-energy calculations at MP2/6-31G*). Data comparing semi-empirical models, Hartree-Fock models and SVWN and pBP density functional models with MP2/6-31G* absolute activation energies (and with experimental values where available) are found in **Table 3-18**.

Semi-empirical calculations are not suitable for absolute activation energy calculations. Calculated values are usually (but not always) larger than experimental (and MP2/6-31G*) activation energies. The mean absolute deviation from MP2/6-31G* for MNDO calculations is nearly twice as large as for either AM1 or PM3 calculations.

Overall, the performance of Hartree-Fock models is also poor. In most cases, activation energies are overestimated by large amounts. This is not surprising in view of previous comparisons involving

Table 3-17: Bond Distances in Transition States (Å)

reaction	parameter	semi-empirical			Hartree-Fock				
		MNDO	AM1	PM3	STO-3G	3-21G	6-31G*	6-31G**	6-31+G*
$H_3C-N\equiv C \longrightarrow N\equiv C-CH_3$	r_1	1.80	1.80	1.83	1.85	1.99	1.90	1.90	1.90
	r_2	1.70	1.70	1.78	1.73	1.87	1.74	1.74	1.75
	r_3	1.22	1.23	1.22	1.22	1.19	1.17	1.17	1.17
	r_1	a	1.40	1.41	1.42	1.40	1.39	1.39	1.39
	r_2	a	1.38	1.37	1.36	1.37	1.38	1.38	1.38
	r_3	a	2.12	2.14	2.22	2.21	2.20	2.20	2.20
	r_4	a	1.38	1.38	1.37	1.38	1.38	1.38	1.39
	r_1	1.45	1.41	1.42	1.39	1.40	1.40	1.40	1.39
	r_2	1.72	1.44	1.51	1.50	1.40	1.31	1.32	1.29
	r_3	1.03	1.18	1.08	1.08	1.24	1.33	1.31	1.37
	r_4	1.30	1.28	1.28	1.26	1.25	1.23	1.25	1.25
	r_5	1.29	1.28	1.28	1.26	1.25	1.23	1.24	1.24
	r_6	1.52	1.76	1.68	1.84	1.97	2.10	2.05	2.16
mean absolute deviation from MP2/6-31G*		0.14	0.06	0.07	0.05	0.04	0.04	0.03	0.04

reaction	parameter	Hartree-Fock		density functional				MP2
		6-311G*	6-311+G**	SVWN/DN*	SVWN/DN**	pBP/DN*	pBP/DN**	6-31G*
H₃C–N≡C → [structure] → N≡C–CH₃	r_1	1.91	1.91	1.74	1.74	1.79	1.79	1.86
	r_2	1.75	1.75	1.76	1.75	1.82	1.82	1.75
	r_3	1.17	1.17	1.20	1.20	1.20	1.20	1.21
[structure]	r_1	1.39	1.39	1.41	1.41	1.41	1.41	1.41
	r_2	1.38	1.38	1.36	1.36	1.39	1.39	1.38
	r_3	2.20	2.19	2.39	2.37	2.32	2.30	2.29
	r_4	1.38	1.39	1.36	1.36	1.39	1.39	1.38
[structure]	r_1	1.39	1.40	1.39	1.39	1.40	1.41	1.40
	r_2	1.29	1.29	1.37	1.35	1.33	1.32	1.34
	r_3	1.36	1.36	1.26	1.26	1.34	1.34	1.29
	r_4	1.24	1.24	1.25	1.27	1.27	1.28	1.27
	r_5	1.23	1.23	1.25	1.26	1.27	1.27	1.27
	r_6	2.15	2.12	1.97	1.95	2.07	2.04	1.98
mean absolute deviation from MP2/6-31G*		0.04	0.04	0.03	0.03	0.03	0.03	–

a) Incorrectly assigns the transition state to be highly asymmetrical, limiting to a diradical description.

81

Table 3-18: Activation Energies (kcal/mol)

reaction	semi-empirical			Hartree-Fock						
	MNDO	AM1	PM3	STO-3G	3-21G(*)	6-31G*	6-31G**	6-31+G*	6-311G*	6-311+G**
$CH_3NC \longrightarrow CH_3CN$	68	83	58	56	58	46	45	46	45	45
$HCO_2CH_2CH_3 \longrightarrow HCO_2H + C_2H_4$	79	64	60	96	62	70	68	69	71	67
(six-membered ring)	40	37	41	56	45	56	56	56	56	57
(oxygen-containing ring)	40	32	35	50	41	48	48	48	48	48
$CF_2 + C_2H_4 \longrightarrow CF_2CH_2CH_2$	22	17	9	23	27	31	32	32	32	32
(cyclopentane $\longrightarrow$)	56	28	32	35	30	40	40	41	41	43
(ring) $+$ C_2H_4	80	67	60	106	75	84	84	84	85	83
$HCNO + C_2H_2$	27	22	41	21	25	35	35	36	36	37
$HBF_2 + C_2H_4 \longrightarrow CH_3CH_2BF_2$	49	50	27	46	35	39	39	40	38	39
$SOH \longrightarrow HOS$	47	24	24	14	24	33	33	33	–	–
(diene)	57	37	37	62	52	56	58	59	59	58
(cyclobutene)	50	35	41	80	42	47	46	45	46	45
(lactone) $\longrightarrow$ $+ CO_2$	85	62	66	108	59	60	60	58	59	58
SO_2 (sulfolene) $\longrightarrow$ $+ SO_2$	83	43	56	66	49	49	49	48	–	–
$(CH_3)_2\overset{+}{N}\text{-}CH_2CH_3 \overset{O^-}{} \longrightarrow (CH_3)_2NOH + C_2H_4$	43	38	37	26	36	45	42	47	46	43
mean absolute deviation from MP2/6-31G*	22	12	11	27	13	19	18	19	19	18

reaction	density functional				MP2	expt.
	SVWN/DN*	SVWN/DN**	pBP/DN*	pBP/DN**	6-31G*	
$CH_3NC \longrightarrow CH_3CN$	42	42	40	40	43	38
$HCO_2CH_2CH_3 \longrightarrow HCO_2H + C_2H_4$	43	42	44	42	60	40,44
(cyclohexene ring opening)	20	22	27	27	31[a]	36
(oxacyclohexene ring opening)	20	21	21	21	25[a]	31
$CF_2 + C_2H_4 \longrightarrow CF_2CH_2CH_2$	0[b]	0[b]	5	5	12	–
(norbornadiene + ethylene)	1	2	16	17	11[a]	20
(cyclopentene + C₂H₄)	48	47	50	48	60	–
$HCNO + C_2H_2 \longrightarrow$ (isoxazole)	1	1	10	10	8	–
$HBF_2 + C_2H_4 \longrightarrow CH_3CH_2BF_2$	4	5	22	22	20	–
$SOH \longrightarrow HOS$	14	12	14	13	17	–
(ring rearrangement)	23	26	30	29	35	–
(cyclobutene → butadiene)	35	34	32	32	37	–
(lactone → + CO_2)	39	39	32	32	45[a]	–
(sulfolene → + SO_2)	30	30	19	19	27[a]	–
$(CH_3)_2N\text{-}CH_2CH_3 \longrightarrow (CH_3)_2NOH + C_2H_4$	17	15	17	15	30[a]	–
mean absolute deviation from MP2/6-31G*	9	9	6	7	–	–

a) Assumes HF/6-31G* reactant and transition-state geometries.
b) No transition state found.

homolytic bond dissociation energies (see **Table 3-9**), which were too small.* STO-3G calculations generally provide the worst results, and 3-21G$^{(*)}$ calculations generally provide the best results, insofar as mean absolute deviation from MP2/6-31G* calculations. Hartree-Fock models with 6-31G* and larger basis sets all yield similar results. Overall, none of the models appear to be suitable for determination of absolute activation energies.

pBP models yield activation energies which are quite close to those from MP2/6-31G* calculations. On the other hand, local density models yield activation energies which are typically smaller than MP2/6-31G* values. Note, in particular, the very small barriers calculated for Diels-Alder and 1,3-dipolar cycloaddition reactions. Note also, that difluorocarbene addition to ethene is incorrectly suggested by the SVWN calculations to occur without barrier. These observations are consistent with the trend previously noted for homolytic bond dissociation energies which were greatly overestimated (see **Table 3-9**). Overall, pBP density functional calculations (but not SVWN calculations) appear to provide a viable, low cost alternative to MP2 calculations.

While knowledge of absolute activation energies is no doubt vital in some situations, there are numerous other situations where it is not. For example, proper accounting of remote substituent effects or regio and/or stereo product distributions does not require knowledge of absolute activation energies, but only accurate relative activation energies. This turns out to be a much easier task, and one for which even relatively simple (and practical) levels of calculation are properly suited.

A good example involves relative activation energies for Diels-Alder cycloadditions of a variety of cyanoethylenes with cyclopentadiene, relative to the addition of acrylonitrile with cyclopentadiene as a standard, i.e.

---

* The reasoning here is that a transition state is typically more tightly bound than the reactants and that correlation effects will be greater.

relative to

or

[ ]‡ denotes the transition state for the reaction. This is an *isodesmic* reaction, and its energy should be well described with Hartree-Fock models, but probably not with semi-empirical models (see **Tables 3-12** to **3-14**). MP2 and density functional models would also be expected to yield acceptable results.

As seen from the data in **Table 3-19**, semi-empirical models provide a poor account; with one exception, they indicate that increasing the electron deficiency of the dienophile leads to an increase in barrier height and not the known decrease. MNDO data have not been provided. As noted previously, this model provides a very poor account of Diels-Alder reactions, yielding transition states which are highly asymmetric.

3-21G, 6-31G* and larger-basis-set Hartree-Fock models accurately reproduce the experimental relative activation energies, although the STO-3G model is not successful. (Calculations using the Hartree-Fock model with the 6-311+G** basis set are prohibitive and have not been performed.) This parallels behavior with the thermochemistry of *isodesmic* processes (see **Tables 3-12** to **3-14**). Note the similarity of Hartree-Fock models beyond the 6-31G* model. As with *isodesmic* thermochemical comparisons, there seems little justification for basis set extensions beyond 6-31G*.

pBP density functional models do not yield entirely acceptable results, in that they underestimate the effect of substitution on lowering the

85

Table 3-19: Relative Activation Energies for Diels-Alder Cycloadditions of Cyclopentadiene with Electron-Deficient Dienophiles (kcal/mol)[a,b]

dienophile	semi-empirical		Hartree-Fock					
	AM1	PM3	STO-3G	3-21G	6-31G*	6-31G**	6-31+G*	6-311G*
trans-1,2-dicyanoethylene	1	1	-1	-4	-3	-3	-3	-3
cis-1,2-dicyanoethylene	2	1	0	-3	-3	-3	-3	-3
1,1-dicyanoethylene	-1	-1	-5	-7	-8	-8	-8	-8
tricyanoethylene	1	2	-4	-8	-9	-9	-10	-10
tetracyanoethylene	2	3	-4	-11	-11	-11	-11	-11

dienophile	density functional		expt.
	pBP/DN*	pBP/DN**	
trans-1,2-dicyanoethylene	-2	-2	-2.6
cis-1,2-dicyanoethylene	-1	0	-3.8
1,1-dicyanoethylene	-7	-7	-7.2
tricyanoethylene	-6	-4	-9.2
tetracyanoethylene	-6	-5	-11.2

a) Activation energy relative to that of reaction of cyclopentadiene with acrylonitrile (*endo* addition).
b) Calculations utilize 6-31G* equilibrium and transition-state geometries.

activation barrier. The reason for this is unclear. SVWN calculations have not been performed, as this model is known, to yield barriers for Diels-Alder reactions which are far too low. Also, calculations using the MP2/6-31G* model are prohibitive in cost and have not been performed.

Regio and stereochemical preferences may also be expressed as *isodesmic* processes. For example, the regioselectivity of (*endo*) addition of 2-methylcyclopentadiene with acrylonitrile comes down to the difference in energy the transition states leading to *meta* and *para* products, respectively, i.e.

or

Similarly, the difference in energy between *syn* and *anti* transition states for (*endo*) addition of 5-methylcyclopentadiene with acrylonitrile accounts for the stereochemistry of this reaction, i.e.

Table 3-20 provides data relating to the regiochemistry of Diels-Alder cycloadditions of 1 and 2-substituted cyclopentadienes with acrylonitrile, and the stereochemistry of cycloadditions of 5-substituted cyclopentadienes with acrylonitrile. The experimental data are limited to the identity of the preferred product (product ratios are unavailable). However, it is known that a methoxy substituent is more effective in directing regiochemistry than a methyl group, and that a substituent on the 1-position is a more effective regiodirector than the same substituent in the 2-position.

Semi-empirical models (AM1 and PM3 only. MNDO would not be expected to give meaningful results; see previous discussion) reproduce the known regiochemical and stereochemical preferences in these systems. They also reproduce the enhanced directing ability of methoxy relative to methyl but, in contrast to experiment, suggest that substituents in the 2-position are more effective regiodirectors than substituents in the 1-position. Both AM1 and PM3 models reproduce the observed stereochemistry for additions of 5-substituted cyclopentadienes and acrylonitrile, although the PM3 model suggests a very weak preference in the case of 5-methoxycyclopentadiene, at odds with the strong preference suggested by other methods (see discussion following).

Hartree-Fock models reproduce all of the experimental "facts". Models with basis sets larger than 6-31G* give nearly identical results to the 6-31G* model, and it is difficult to justify their use for this purpose. (Calculations using the 6-311+G** basis set are prohibitive in cost and have not been performed.)

The only correlated models considered are the pBP/DN* and pBP/DN** models. The MP2/6-31G* model is prohibitive in cost and SVWN models would not be expected to yield meaningful results (see previous discussion). Both of these models reproduce the known reactivity trends. The numerical data are, in fact, quite close to those from Hartree-Fock models, except that predicted product ratios are generally more modest. Except perhaps for cost (pBP models), there is little to justify use of correlated models for this purpose.

Table 3-20: Relative Activation Energies for Regio and Stereospecific Diels-Alder Cycloadditions of Substituted Cyclopentadienes with Acrylonitrile (kcal/mol)[a]

substituent on cyclopentadiene	semi-empirical		STO-3G	3-21G	Hartree-Fock				observed major regio/stereo product
	AM1	PM3			6-31G*	6-31G**	6-31+G*	6-311G*	
1-methyl	0.7	0.4	1.0	0.9	1.3	1.3	1.3	1.3	*ortho*
1-methoxy	1.9	1.1	2.7	3.3	4.2	4.2	4.1	4.3	*ortho*
2-methyl	0.9	0.9	0.6	0.1	0.6	0.6	0.8	0.7	*para*
2-methoxy	2.4	1.8	2.5	2.9	4.0	3.9	4.4	4.1	*para*
5-methyl	2.0	0.8	3.1	2.5	1.1	0.9	0.7	0.7	*anti*
5-methoxy	1.8	0.3	3.2	9.0	6.6	6.7	6.5	7.0	*syn*

substituent on cyclopentadiene	density functional		observed major regio/stereo product
	pBP/DN*	pBP/DN**	
1-methyl	1.6	1.5	*ortho*
1-methoxy	5.3	5.1	*ortho*
2-methyl	0.5	0.3	*para*
2-methoxy	3.3	3.3	*para*
5-methyl	1.1	1.0	*anti*
5-methoxy	5.0	5.1	*syn*

a) Numerical values indicate energies of minor product relative to experimentally observed major product. Positive numbers indicate regio and stereochemical assignments in accord with experiment. Products for 1-substituted systems are *ortho/meta*; for 2-substituted systems are *para/meta*; for 5-substituted systems are *syn/anti*.

89

Atomic Charges and Dipole Moments

Atomic charges are a familiar and important component of the everyday language of chemists. Charge distributions indicate where the electrons reside in molecules, which in turn suggests their "chemistry". Despite their obvious utility, there is actually no way either to measure atomic charges or to calculate them (at least not uniquely). The reason is simple to understand. From the point of view of quantum mechanics, a molecule is made up of nuclei, each of which bears a positive charge equal to its atomic number, and electrons, each of which bears a charge of -1. While the nuclei can be treated as point charges, i.e., they do not occupy appreciable space, electrons need to be viewed in terms of a distribution of negative charge. This distribution is primarily concentrated in regions around the individual nuclei and in between nuclei that are close together, i.e., are bonded, although it extends throughout all space. To assign a charge on an atom, it is necessary to partition the total electron distribution by atoms. There is no unique way to accomplish this. However, a number of different "recipes" have been proposed for calculating charges, among them the so-called **Mulliken population analysis**[2], leading to **Mulliken** charges and a fitting of the **electrostatic potential** (the energy of interaction of a positive point charge with the nuclei and electrons of a molecule), leading to **electrostatic charges**[3].

Dipole moments can be measured experimentally, and reflect overall charge distributions in molecules. Therefore, they can be employed to judge the relative merits of one level of calculation over another in describing overall charge distribution. Calculated dipole moments for molecules incorporating heteroatoms are compared with experimental values in **Table 3-21**. A number of interesting trends are found in these compounds. For example, the dipole moments in trimethylamine is less than that in ammonia while that in trimethylphosphine is greater than that in phosphine. A similar reversal is found in comparing dipole moments between oxygen and sulfur compounds.

The MMFF94 model yields atomic charges, which may then be used to obtain a dipole moment. It is, in fact, perhaps the simplest procedure for establishing dipole moments, and may be especially attractive in dealing with large molecules. While absolute dipole moments obtained from MMFF94 are not in very good agreement with the experimental data (they are typically too large by 0.5 - 1 debye), trends appear to be reproduced. Note, in particular, the reduction in dipole moment from ammonia to trimethylamine and the increase in dipole moment from phosphine to trimethylphosphine.

AM1 and PM3 semi-empirical models do not provide a good account of dipole moments. Not only are individual errors often very large, but observed trends in dipole moments with differing substitution are frequently not correctly reproduced. In general, results for molecules with first-row elements are better than for those with second-row elements. The MNDO (MNDO/d) model provides a much better account, in large part due to improved description of molecules incorporating second-row elements. d-functions on second-row elements and/or improved parameterization may be responsible.

Hartree-Fock models are moderately successful in reproducing trends in dipole moments, given that split-valence or polarization basis sets are employed. The STO-3G model properly accounts of dipole moment changes in nitrogen and oxygen compounds, but fails to reproduce them in phosphorous and sulfur compounds. This parallels the generally poor performance of STO-3G for molecules incorporating second-row elements (see **Table 3-3**), and may be due to the lack of d functions on second-row elements. Note, that Hartree-Fock dipole moments are uniformly larger than experimental values, typically by 20 to 30% for all basis sets. Beyond 6-31G*, Hartree-Fock models all produce similar dipole moments.

The MP2/6-31G* model also performs well for the calculation of dipole moments. As might be expected, these are usually (but not always) smaller than dipole moments resulting from 6-31G* Hartree-Fock calculations. Recall that correlation models involve promotion of electrons from filled orbitals into empty orbitals, that is, they take electrons from "where they are" (negative regions) to "where they are not" (positive regions). This implies a decrease in overall charge separation and a corresponding reduction in dipole moment.

Table 3-21: Dipole Moments for Molecules Incorporating Heteroatoms (debyes)

molecule	molecular mechanics	semi-empirical			Hartree-Fock				
	MMFF94	MNDO	AM1	PM3	STO-3G	3-21G(*)	6-31G*	6-31G**	6-31+G*
NH_3	2.04	1.75	1.85	1.55	1.87	1.75	1.92	1.84	1.86
NMe_3	1.80	0.75	1.02	1.15	1.13	0.89	0.75	0.74	0.76
H_2O	2.46	1.78	1.86	1.74	1.71	2.39	2.20	2.15	2.29
Me_2O	2.15	1.27	1.43	1.25	1.33	1.85	1.48	1.47	1.56
△O	2.25	1.92	1.91	1.77	1.46	2.78	2.28	2.27	2.35
PH_3	1.03	0.12	2.29	1.18	0.60	0.87	0.88	0.89	0.85
PMe_3	2.06	1.20	1.52	1.08	0.30	1.28	1.37	1.38	1.40
H_2S	1.59	1.06	1.86	1.78	1.03	1.41	1.41	1.39	1.44
Me_2S	2.61	1.54	1.56	1.96	0.87	1.75	1.80	1.80	1.85
△S	2.63	1.69	2.12	2.36	0.75	2.12	2.31	2.32	2.35
thiophene	1.32	0.18	0.34	0.67	0.10	0.76	0.90	0.90	0.81
mean absolute error	0.68	0.15	0.40	0.32	0.42	0.37	0.32	0.31	0.34

molecule	Hartree-Fock		MP2	density functional		expt.
	6-311G*	6-311+G**	6-31G*	pBP/DN*	pBP/DN**	
NH_3	1.84	1.73	1.97	1.95	1.78	1.47
NMe_3	0.66	0.74	0.74	0.55	0.53	0.61
H_2O	2.32	2.20	2.20	2.20	2.08	1.85
Me_2O	1.44	1.54	1.44	1.36	1.31	1.30
△O	2.18	2.25	2.11	2.03	2.02	1.89
PH_3	0.80	0.85	1.00	0.91	0.80	0.58
PMe_3	1.42	1.41	1.41	1.20	1.19	1.19
H_2S	1.43	1.38	1.48	1.43	1.31	0.97
Me_2S	1.85	1.83	1.75	1.58	1.55	1.50
△S	2.38	2.33	2.10	1.94	1.92	1.85
thiophene (S)	0.85	0.81	0.53	0.40	0.39	0.55
mean absolute error	0.31	0.30	0.27	0.20	0.15	–

Dipole moments obtained from pBP density functional models[*] are also usually larger than Hartree-Fock dipole moments, and are generally very similar to those from MP2/6-31G* calculations. As such, they are in reasonable accord with the experimental data.

Relative Computation Times for Models

The second important consideration in the selection of an appropriate molecular mechanics or quantum chemical model is its "cost". It is not possible to estimate precisely how much computer time a particular calculation will require, as many factors remain uncertain. It is possible, however, to provide representative examples to help distinguish applications which are practical from those which are clearly not. Relative times obtained using SPARTAN for the MMFF94 molecular mechanics model, the AM1 semi-empirical model, Hartree-Fock models with STO-3G, 3-21G, 6-31G*, 6-31G**, 6-31+G*, 6-311G* and 6-311+G** basis sets, the MP2/6-31G* model, and pBP/DN* and pBP/DN** density functional models, for both energy calculations and geometry optimizations, for methylcyclohexane (a typical "small molecule") and (where not prohibitive) for morphine and (a typical "large molecule") are given in **Table 3-22**. These are relative to times for 3-21G energy calculations on methylcyclohexane and morphine, respectively.

Molecular mechanics calculations are at least an order of magnitude less costly than the simplest (semi-empirical) quantum chemical calculations, and the ratio between the two increases rapidly with increasing molecular size. Molecular mechanics is really the only viable alternative at present for molecules comprising more than a few hundred atoms. It is also likely to be the only practical alternative for conformation searching on molecules with more than two or three degrees of freedom.

The cost of evaluating the energy using the 3-21G model is more than an order of magnitude greater than that for obtaining an equilibrium geometry using the AM1 semi-empirical model. This

---

*   Dipole moments calculated using the SVWN and pBP models are the same, because non-local corrections introduced pertubatively following convergence of the local density model affect only the energy and not the density matrix (from which the dipole moment is obtained).

Table 3-22: Relative Computation Times[a]

level of calculation	task	
	single-point energy	geometry optimization[b,c]
equatorial methylcyclohexane (C_7H_{14}, C_s symmetry, 32 independent variables)		
MMFF94[c]	f	f
AM1[d]	f	.06
STO-3G	0.4	3
3-21G	**1**	8
6-31G*	7	54
6-31G**	14	100
6-31+G*	13	110
6-311G*	14	110
6-311+G**	44	310
pBP/DN*[e]	2	14
pBP/DN**[e]	3	23
MP2/6-31G*	100	–
morphine ($C_7H_{19}NO_3$, C_1 symmetry, 114 independent variables)		
MMFF94[c]	f	f
AM1[d]	f	.03
STO-3G	0.3	9
3-21G	**1**[g]	17
6-31G*	7	106
6-31G**	9	–
pBP/DN*[e]	1	12
pBP/DN**[e]	1	15

a) Using SPARTAN version 5.1 on a Silicon Graphics Octane.
b) Using or starting from MMFF94 equilibrium geometry and Hessian.
c) SYBYL mechanics is of comparable speed.
d) MNDO and PM3 semi-empirical are of comparable speed.
e) SVWN density functional is of comparable speed.
f) Too small to measure.
g) 3-21G single-energy calculation on morphine requires approximately 42 times more computer time than 3-21G calculation on *equatorial* methylcyclohexane.

ratio should maintain with larger molecules, as both semi-empirical and Hartree-Fock models scale as the cube of size (for sufficiently large molecules).* Geometry optimization using 3-21G is approximately an order of magnitude more costly than energy calculation, and this difference would be expected to increase with increasing size, due to an increase in the number of geometrical variables. The cost difference for both energy evaluation and geometry optimization between 3-21G and 6-31G* calculations is on the order of six or seven times for both molecules. Addition of polarization functions, addition of diffuse functions on heavy atoms or increased valence shell splitting all lead to a doubling of the cost of a Hartree-Fock calculation. All three taken together lead to an increase in cost of six to seven times. While comparisons only for methylcyclohexane are available, these differences would be expected to increase with increasing molecular size.

MP2 calculations (single energy for methylcyclohexane only) lead to an increase in cost of more than an order of magnitude over comparable (same basis set) Hartree-Fock treatments. This ratio would be expected to increase very rapidly with increasing molecular size. The cost of evaluating the energy using MP2/6-31G* is approximately double the cost of a full structure optimization using the 6-31G* Hartree-Fock model for methylcyclohexane.

Comparisons involving "equal size" basis sets (DN* with 6-31G*) show that the pBP calculations are between three and seven times faster than Hartree-Fock calculations. A more appropriate comparison is between density functional and MP2 calculations with comparable basis sets. (Actually, experience suggests that the DN* basis set is "superior" to 6-31G* in molecular calculations and roughly equivalent to the larger 6-311G* basis set, see **Appendix B** of **Chapter 2**) Unfortunately, MP2 calculations on any but the smallest systems are prohibitive. The ratio of MP2/6-31G* to pBP/DN* calculation

---

* In practice, Hartree-Fock models scale at an even lower power of size (number of basis functions), perhaps as low as 2.5. Semi-empirical models appear to maintain a cube dependence. Density functional models scale formally as the cube of the number of basis functions, but in practice scale as the 2.2 to 2.4 power for large systems. MP2 models scale as the fifth power of size, and this dependence appears to be maintained with increase in size.

times for methylcyclohexane is already 50, and this difference would be expected to increase dramatically for larger molecules. Clearly the advantage goes to density functional models.

Recommendations

Taking both quality of results and "cost" into account, is it possible to say with certainty which model is the "best" for a particular application? Probably not, although rough guidelines can certainly be set.

Table 3-23 provides an overview of the classes of methods discussed in this guide (molecular mechanics, semi-empirical, Hartree-Fock, MP2 and density functional) with regard to the calculation of equilibrium and transition-state geometries, conformations and reaction energetics. For each task, the methods are "graded": **G** (good), **P** (poor) and **GC** (good with cautious application). While the grading is very rough, it allows the obvious trends to be exposed. As a reminder, "cost comparisons" are also included.

A number of conclusions may easily be drawn:

i) All models provide a good account of molecular equilibrium geometries for organic molecules and, where they are applicable, of transition-state geometries. This is not to suggest that all models are equal in this regard, but rather that all meet "minimum standards". In particular, low-cost molecular mechanics and semi-empirical molecular orbital models often provide very good equilibrium geometries, and only rarely yield very poor geometries. They should be used for this purpose wherever possible. At the very least, they should be employed to furnish "guess geometries" to start higher-level calculations.

Hartree-Fock models with basis sets larger than 6-31G* do not provide significantly improved descriptions of either equilibrium or transition-state geometries over the Hartree-Fock 6-31G* model and, in most cases, the 3-21G model. Note, however, that MP2 and density functional models using split-valence basis sets would not be expected to yield suitable geometries. Correlated models require at the very least basis

Table 3-23: Performance and Cost of Models

task	molecular mechanics	semi-empirical	density functional SVWN	density functional pBP	Hartree-Fock	MP2
geometry (organic)	GC	G	G	G	G	G
geometry (transition metals)	P	G	G	G	P	?
transition-state geometry	N/A	G	G	G	G	G
conformation	G	P	GC	G	GC	G
thermochemistry (non *isodesmic*)	N/A	P	GC	G	GC	G
thermochemistry (*isodesmic*)	N/A	P	G	G	G	G
cost	very low	low	moderate	moderate	high	very high

G = good GC = good with cautious application P = poor ? = unknown N/A = not applicable sets which incorporate polarization functions.

Hartree-Fock models are not reliable for geometry calculations on compounds incorporating transition metals, but the PM3 semi-empirical model and density functional models provide good accounts. The performance of the MP2 model for this purpose remains to be established, although it would be expected to be good.

ii) Hartree-Fock models (6-31G* and larger basis sets), MP2 models and density functional models all generally provide good descriptions of conformational energy differences in organic compounds. MP2 and pBP models are the most reliable and, given the large difference in cost between them, practical applications on any but the smallest systems are probably better handled using pBP methods.

Semi-empirical models may be suitable for identifying conformational minima, and for determining the geometries of these minima, but they are clearly not suitable at providing accurate relative conformer energies.

The MMFF94 molecular mechanics model appears to do an excellent job in reproducing known conformational energy differences in organic compounds. On the other hand, SYBYL mechanics does not provide an acceptable account of conformational energy differences. It should not be used for this purpose.

There is no experience with conformational energy differences for transition-metal inorganic and organometallic compounds.

iii) Hartree-Fock, MP2 and pBP models provide an excellent account of the energetics of *isodesmic* reactions. On the basis of cost alone, it is very difficult to justify use of MP2 for this purpose.

MP2 and pBP models are generally the more reliable for describing the energetics of non-*isodesmic* reactions although, except for reactions which involve explicit bond making or breaking, the 6-31G* and larger-basis-set Hartree-Fock models (and to a lesser extent the 3-21G$^{(*)}$ model) also yield acceptable results. Hartree-Fock models with basis sets larger than 6-31G* generally yield reaction energies which are nearly identical to those from the Hartree-Fock 6-31G* model.

MP2 and pBP models are needed to accurately account for the energetics of reactions where bonds are broken or formed and, by implication, to properly describe absolute activation energies. Hartree-Fock and local density functional models are unsatisfactory for this purpose. This is an important area of application for correlated (MP2 and density functional) models. Cost considerations suggest the latter may be preferred for routine applications. Hartree-Fock models are, however, satisfactory in description of relative activation energies.

Semi-empirical models are unsatisfactory in their description of the energetics of all types of reactions, *isodesmic* processes included.

References

1. L.A. Curtiss, K. Raghavhari, G.W. Trucks and J.A. Pople, *J. Chem. Phys.*, **94**, 7221 (1991).
2. R.S. Mulliken, *J. Chem. Phys.*, **23** 1833, 1841, 2338, 2343 (1955).
3. L.E. Chirlian and M.M. Francl, *J. Computational Chem.*, **8**, 894 (1987); C.M. Breneman and K.B. Wiberg, *ibid.*, **11**, 361 (1990).

Chapter 4

Using Models

This chapter addresses a number of practical issues which arise in applying molecular mechanics calculations, semi-empirical and Hartree-Fock molecular orbital calculations, and correlated MP2 and density functional calculations to the investigation of molecular structures and stabilities and chemical reactivities. It proposes "strategies" which combine different methods in order to achieve the desired goal with the least amount of effort.

Methods available for calculation of molecular structures, relative thermochemical stabilities, and other properties differ in "cost" of application by several orders of magnitude (see **Table 3-22**). Molecular mechanics and semi-empirical molecular orbital methods are the least costly and correlated methods such as the MP2 model are the most costly. In between, are Hartree-Fock models and density functional models. While in general, the most costly methods provide the best overall descriptions, comparisons provided in the previous chapter suggest that semi-empirical and small-basis-set Hartree-Fock models usually perform quite well in certain tasks, and further that density functional models are, more often than not the equal to the MP2 model. For example, equilibrium and transition-state geometries appear to be well described even with semi-empirical models and certainly with Hartree-Fock models. Might these structures replace geometries from higher-level calculations for relative energy and property calculations? Also, while semi-empirical methods provide a poor account of reaction energetics, Hartree-Fock models, even small-basis-set Hartree-Fock models, often perform well, except in situations where there is net bond making or breaking. Is it possible to formulate energetic comparisons which avoid this pitfall? And, for those comparisons which necessarily involve bond making or breaking, might density functional models replace the MP2 model?

Topics such as these are the subjects of the present chapter. In keeping with the remainder of this guide, treatment is very brief and only a few "representative" examples are provided. Expanded treatment is available elsewhere.[1]

Using Approximate Equilibrium Geometries[*]

Is it always necessary to utilize "exact" equilibrium geometries in carrying out thermochemical comparisons, or can geometries obtained from molecular mechanics and semi-empirical calculations be substituted without adverse consequences? This is a very important question given that optimization of equilibrium structure can easily require an order of magnitude (or more) computation than an energy (property) calculation at a single geometry (see **Table 3-22**). Rephrased, the question might read: *"Is the substantial added effort required to produce a proper optimized structure effort well spent?"*

The question is addressed here by constructing two different series of thermochemical comparisons. Comparisons among structural isomers illustrate processes in which only the total number of electron pairs is conserved (and not the numbers of each kind of bond or lone pair). Bond separation reactions illustrate *isodesmic* processes, that is, reactions in which the total number of each kind of chemical bond is conserved and only the local environments are altered.

The data in **Table 4-1** assesses the effect of choice of geometry on the relative stabilities of structural isomers as calculated using the MP2/6-31G* model. The conclusion is quite clear. Substitution of 6-31G*, AM1 and MMFF94 geometries for MP2/6-31G* structures is of little consequence; maximum errors are 2 kcal/mol for use of both 6-31G* and AM1 geometries, and 5 kcal/mol for use of MMFF94 geometries. These are smaller than errors of any of the models in comparison with experimental data.

---

[*]   The nomenclature "model A//model B" is commonly used to designate a property calculation at one level of theory (model A) based on a geometry at another (simpler) level of theory (model B).

Table 4-1: Effect of Choice of Geometry on Relative Energies of Structural Isomers from MP2/6-31G* Calculations (kcal/mol)

isomer	geometry				
	MMFF94	AM1	6-31G*	MP2/6-31G*	expt.
C_2H_3N (relative to acetonitrile)					
methyl isocyanide	28	29	27	29	21
C_2H_4O (relative to acetaldehyde)					
oxirane	28	27	27	27	26
C_3H_4 (relative to propyne)					
allene	5	3	4	5	2
cyclopropene	28	22	22	23	22
C_3H_6 (relative to propene)					
cyclopropane	4	4	4	4	7
C_3H_6O (relative to acetone)					
propanal	6	6	6	6	7
allyl alcohol	30	29	29	29	22
methyl, vinyl ether	30	30	30	30	26
oxetane	33	32	32	33	31
mean absolute error	4	3	3	3	–
mean absolute error due to use of approximate geometry	1	0	1	–	–

A similar comparison, this time involving the energetics of bond separation reactions obtained from pBP/DN* calculations, is provided in **Table 4-2**. MMFF94, AM1 and 3-21G geometries have been used. Overall the errors are very small; the largest error resulting from the use of 3-21G or 6-31G* geometries is 1 kcal/mol, and from the use of either AM1 or MMFF94 geometries is 3 kcal/mol.

These two examples clearly suggest that the use of "approximate" equilibrium geometries does not generally lead to significant errors in reaction energy calculations. While situations where different levels of calculation lead to very different equilibrium geometries no doubt exist, and would certainly cause more sizable errors, these do not appear to be common. More than anything else, the decision of whether or not to use approximate geometries comes down to a matter of cost. Molecular mechanics and semi-empirical calculations will always be less costly than Hartree-Fock, MP2 and density functional calculations, irrespective of molecular size. Small-basis-set Hartree-Fock calculations (such as 3-21G and 6-31G* calculations) will always be less costly than MP2 calculations, but may be comparable in cost to density functional calculations. Density functional calculations will always be less costly than MP2 calculations.

Some properties show greater sensitivity to geometry than energy, perhaps most important among them dipole moments. For example, the data in **Table 4-3** for the MP2/6-31G* model shows that dipole moments in nitrogen, oxygen and sulfur containing compounds are quite sensitive to exact choice of equilibrium geometry (MMFF94, AM1 and 6-31G* structures being substituted for MP2/6-31G* geometries). Errors are mostly small (outside the range of agreement between calculated and experimental dipole moments), although in some cases they are sizable.

"Exact" equilibrium structures *must be used* for the calculation of vibrational frequencies, as well as thermodynamic properties such as entropies obtained from calculated frequencies. This is because the frequencies derive from the second derivative term, E'', in a Taylor series expansion of the total energy.

Table 4-2: Effect of Choice of Geometry on Energies of Bond Separation Reactions from pBP/DN* Calculations (kcal/mol)

bond separation reaction	geometry				
	MMFF94	AM1	3-21G	pBP/DN*	expt.
$CH_3CH_2NH_2 + CH_4 \rightarrow CH_3CH_3 + CH_3NH_2$	4	4	4	3	3
$CH_3CH_2OH + CH_4 \rightarrow CH_3CH_3 + CH_3OH$	6	5	5	5	5
$CH_3CH=CH_2 + CH_4 \rightarrow CH_3CH_3 + CH_2=CH_2$	6	5	5	5	5
$CH_3CHO + CH_4 \rightarrow CH_3CH_3 + H_2CO$	12	12	12	11	11
$NH_2CHO + CH_4 \rightarrow CH_3NH_2 + H_2CO$	36	35	35	34	30
△ $+ 3CH_4 \rightarrow 3CH_3CH_3$	-19	-19	-20	-21	-22
△NH $+ 2CH_4 + NH_3 \rightarrow CH_3CH_3 + 2CH_3NH_2$	-13	-14	-16	-16	-17
△O $+ 2CH_4 + H_2O \rightarrow CH_3CH_3 + 2CH_3OH$	-10	-10	-12	-12	-14
mean absolute error	3	2	2	1	-
mean absolute error due to use of approximate geometry	2	2	1	-	-

105

Table 4-3: Effect of Choice of Geometry on Dipole Moments for Molecules Incorporating Heteroatoms from MP2/6-31G* Calculations (debyes)

molecule	geometry					expt.
	MMFF94	AM1	6-31G*	MP2/6-31G*		
NH_3	2.00	1.80	1.92	1.97		1.47
NMe_3	0.81	0.54	0.65	0.74		0.61
H_2O	2.20	2.20	2.16	2.20		1.85
Me_2O	1.43	1.37	1.33	1.44		1.30
△O	2.04	2.01	1.97	2.11		1.89
PH_3	0.98	1.12	1.03	1.00		0.58
PMe_3	1.49	1.49	1.44	1.41		1.19
H_2S	1.48	1.50	1.49	1.48		0.97
Me_2S	1.77	1.67	1.78	1.75		1.50
△S	1.80	1.99	2.10	2.10		1.85
⬠S	0.46	0.46	0.63	0.53		0.55
mean absolute error	0.33	0.25	0.26	0.28		–
mean absolute error due to use of approximate geometry	0.06	0.09	0.06	-		–

106

$$E = E° + E' + E'' + \ldots \qquad (1)$$

Here, $E°$ is a constant, and E' (the first derivative term) is assumed to be rigorously zero. (Higher-order terms are also generally ignored.) Frequencies evaluated at non-equilibrium structures are meaningless!

Using Approximate Transition-State Geometries

A closely related question concerns the need to use "exact" transition-state (and reactant) geometries in determining absolute activation energies. As with thermochemical comparisons, this comes down to balancing the possible magnitude of errors introduced as a result of using approximate geometries vs. the potentially enormous savings in computer time realized by employing low-level models to establish structure, in particular the structure of the transition state. On the one hand, it is to be expected that transition-state geometries will show much greater sensitivity to choice of calculation level than equilibrium geometries (see **Table 3-17**). On the other hand, the potential energy surface in the vicinity of a transition state would be expected to be much "flatter" than that in the vicinity of an equilibrium structure.[*] Therefore, a large change in transition-state geometry from one calculation level to another may lead to only a small change in energy.

Absolute activation energies for a small selection of reactions obtained from the pBP/DN* density functional model using AM1, 3-21G$^{(*)}$ and "exact" (pBP/DN*) reactant and transition-state geometries are provided in **Table 4-4**. In general, use of approximate structures leads only to small errors in calculated activation energies. The largest discrepancy caused by use of 3-21G$^{(*)}$ reactant and transition-state geometries is only 3 kcal/mol, and is typically only 1-2 kcal/mol. Significantly larger errors are seen in a few cases for substitution of AM1 geometries for "exact" structures. The largest discrepancy is 10 kcal/mol, but errors are typically in the range of 1-3 kcal/mol.

The data present a strong case for the use of small-basis-set Hartree-Fock models such as 3-21G$^{(*)}$ to supply reactant and transition-state

---

[*] The argument here is that a transition state is a point on the potential energy surface in which bond making and bond breaking are delicately balanced, compared to an equilibrium structure in which bonding is at a maximum.

Table 4-4: **Effect of Choice of Geometry on Activation Energies from pBP/DN* Calculations (kcal/mol)**

reaction	geometry			
	AM1	3-21G$^{(*)}$	pBP/DN*	expt.
$CH_3NC \longrightarrow CH_3CN$	41	40	40	38
$HCO_2CH_2CH_3 \longrightarrow HCO_2H + C_2H_4$	47	43	42	40,44
(cyclohexadiene) ⟶ (cyclohexene ring)	36	27	27	36
(pyran diene) ⟶ (pyran)	31	21	21	31
$CF_2 + C_2H_4 \longrightarrow \overline{CF_2CH_2CH_2}$	4	5	5	-
(cyclopentadiene) + ‖ ⟶ (norbornene)	18	16	17	20
(cyclohexene, H) ⟶ (butadiene) + C_2H_4	48	49	48	-
$HCNO + C_2H_2 \longrightarrow$ (isoxazole, N–O ring)	9	13	10	-
$HBF_2 + C_2H_4 \longrightarrow CH_3CH_2BF_2$	28	23	22	-
(allyl)SOH $\longrightarrow$ HOS(allyl)	18	11	13	-
(cis-diene) ⟶ (cyclohexadiene)	29	28	29	-
(cyclobutane) ⟶ (2 ethylene)	31	31	32	-
(pyranone)=O ⟶ (butadiene) + CO_2	29	32	32	-
(ring)SO_2 ⟶ (butadiene) + SO_2	10	18	19	-
$(CH_3)_2\overset{+}{N}(O^-)\text{-}CH_2CH_3 \longrightarrow (CH_3)_2NOH + C_2H_4$	19	15	15	-
mean absolute error due to use of approximate reactant and transition-state geometries	4	1	-	-

geometries for activation energy calculations using correlated models. Where cost is a factor, it may be advisable to seriously consider their use. Semi-empirical geometries are less successful for this purpose, and some caution needs to be exercised in their application. Unfortunately, molecular mechanics calculations are not applicable here, as force fields have only been parameterized to reproduce the geometries and conformations of stable molecules and not those of transition states.

Dealing with Flexible Molecules

One of the most difficult problems encountered in real applications involves dealing with flexible molecules. There are actually two different issues to be considered: first identifying the appropriate conformer[*] and then finding it.

The problem of identification of appropriate conformer (lowest energy or global minimum vs. most reactive) will not be addressed here. Rather the appropriate conformer will be assumed to be the lowest-energy conformer, or global minimum. The focus of discussion will be on finding this conformer. For simple systems, with only one or a few degrees of conformational freedom, finding the lowest-energy conformer means examining each and every possibility. This is not practical for systems with many degrees of freedom, where stochastic or molecular dynamics techniques, which do not guarantee location of the lowest-energy structure, are the only alternatives.

In practice, molecular mechanics procedures may be the only choice to survey the full conformational energy surface for a complex molecule, and to identify the most likely low-energy conformers. Even semi-empirical methods are likely to be too costly for extensive conformational calculations on systems with more than a few degrees of freedom. Note, however, that even if semi-empirical methods were practical for this task, the data provided in **Tables 3-15** and **3-16**, indicate that these are not likely to lead to acceptable results. Hartree-Fock and correlated calculations, which should lead to good results,

---

[*]   This is not as obvious as it may seem as the most reactive conformer is not necessarily (and not usually) the most stable conformer.

seem out of the question for any but the very simplest systems. Fortunately, the MMFF94 molecular mechanics model is quite successful in assigning low energy conformers and in providing quantitative estimates of conformer energy differences (see **Tables 3-15** and **3-16**). It would appear to be the method of choice for large scale conformational surveys.

Having identified an appropriate set of low-energy conformers, considerable cost savings might be achieved by using molecular mechanics, semi-empirical or even small-basis-set Hartree-Fock models to furnish geometries of the individual conformers, and only then performing single energy calculations with larger-basis-set Hartree-Fock or with correlated methods.

The effect of choice of equilibrium geometry on MP2/6-31G* conformational energy differences is exemplified by the data in **Table 4-5**. Here, MMFF94, AM1 and 6-31G* geometries have been substituted for MP2/6-31G* structures. Energy differences based on use of Hartree-Fock 6-31G* structures are in nearly perfect accord with those obtained using MP2/6-31G* geometries. The ground-state conformations of all systems are properly reproduced, and the largest energy deviation is only 0.1 kcal/mol. AM1 geometries are not as satisfactory. While the proper ground-state conformation is assigned in all cases, deviations from full MP2/6-31G* calculations of upwards of 1 kcal/mol occur. Use of MMFF94 geometries in place of MP2/6-31G* structures leads to relatively small errors, larger than those resulting from use of Hartree-Fock 6-31G* geometries, but smaller than those resulting from use of AM1 geometries.

Making Effective Use of Energy Data for Thermochemical and Kinetic Comparisons

Is has been shown in **Chapter 3** that correlated models, in particular, MP2 and pBP models, are required to properly account for the energetics of reactions in which the total number of electron pairs (bonds + nonbonded lone pairs) changes (see **Table 3-9**). On the other hand, Hartree-Fock models, even small-basis-set Hartree-Fock models, generally provide good descriptions of reaction energetics where bonds

110

Table 4-5: Effect of Choice of Geometry on Conformational Energy Differences in Acyclic Systems from MP2/6-31G* Calculations (kcal/mol)

molecule	low-energy/ high-energy conformer	geometry				
		MMFF94	AM1	6-31G*	MP2/6-31G*	expt.
n-butane	*trans/gauche*	0.5	1.0	0.7	0.7	0.77
1-butene	*skew/cis*	0.5	0.3	0.5	0.5	0.2
1,3-butadiene	*trans/gauche*	3.0	3.7	2.7	2.6	1.7>2,2.5
acrolein	*trans/cis*	1.3	1.6	1.4	1.5	2.0,2.06
N-methylformamide	*trans/cis*	1.7	1.8	1.2	1.3	1.45
N-methylacetamide	*trans/cis*	2.8	3.3	2.6	2.7	2.3,2.8
formic acid	*cis/trans*	6.0	5.8	5.9	5.9	3.90
methyl formate	*cis/trans*	6.3	7.6	6.3	6.4	3.85,4.75
methyl acetate	*cis/trans*	9.1	9.6	8.8	8.9	8.5
propanal	*cis/skew*	1.5	1.9	1.4	1.4	0.67,0.95
1,2-difluoroethane	*gauche/anti*	0.2	0.0	0.2	0.2	0.8
1,2-dichloroethane	*anti/gauche*	1.5	1.5	1.5	1.5	1.16
ethanol	*anti/gauche*	0.1	0.1	-0.1	-0.1	0.12, 0.4
methyl ethyl ether	*anti/gauche*	1.4	1.8	1.4	1.4	1.5
methyl vinyl ether	*cis/skew*	2.6	3.0	2.8	2.8	1.7
mean absolute error		0.7	0.9	0.6	0.6	-
mean absolute error due to use of approximate geometry		0.1	0.4	0.0	-	-

are not broken or formed. In particular, the energetics of *isodesmic* reactions, in which the number of each kind of chemical bond is maintained, are very well described (see **Tables 3-12** to **3-14**).

A **bond separation reaction** is an *isodesmic* reaction which "breaks down" any molecule comprising three or more heavy (non-hydrogen) atoms, and which can be represented in terms of a classical valence structure, into the simplest set of two-heavy-atom molecules containing the same component bonds. For example, the bond separation reaction for methylhydrazine breaks the molecule into methylamine and hydrazine, the simplest molecules incorporating CN and NN single bonds, respectively.

$$CH_3NHNH_2 + NH_3 \longrightarrow CH_3NH_2 + NH_2NH_2$$

A molecule of ammonia is added to the left to achieve stoichiometric balance.

The bond separation energy is a unique attribute of the molecule, or more precisely, a unique attribute of a given valence description of the molecule. This is, of course, an advantage but it is also a liability, as it forces description in terms of a single conventional valence structure. Because it is not always possible to write a unique valence structure, there will be cases when the bond separation reaction is not unique. Delocalized systems are the most problematic, especially in cases where no single valence structure offers a completely satisfactory description. Ions and free radicals also present problems, and transition states are not subject to treatment in this manner.

Given that Hartree-Fock, MP2 and pBP density functional models provide excellent descriptions of the energetics of bond separation reactions (see **Table 3-12**), and given that thermochemical data for nearly all molecules which appear on the right of bond separation reactions are known experimentally (or may be determined accurately from high-level calculations), means that heats of formation may be accurately established by combining calculated results and experimental (or high-level calculated) data. For example, the heat of formation of methylhydrazine may be obtained from the following thermochemical cycle.

112

$$\Delta H_f(CH_3NHNH_2) = -\Delta E_{rx} - \Delta H_f(NH_3) + \Delta H_f(CH_3NH_2) + \Delta H_f(NH_2NH_2)$$

Here, ΔE_{rx} is the calculated energy of the bond separation reaction and $\Delta H_f(NH_3)$, $\Delta H_f(CH_3NH_2)$ and $\Delta H_f(NH_2NH_2)$ are experimental heats of formation. Heats of formation determined in this way for a number of simple molecules using 6-31G*, MP2/6-31G* and pBP/DN* models are compared with experimental values in **Table 4-6**. The errors are in the range of 2-4 kcal/mol (the same as observed for the bond separation energies). Data from smaller-basis-set Hartree-Fock models and SVWN density functional models would produce similar (but slightly larger) errors, while semi-empirical models would generally lead to errors of unacceptable magnitude.

The overall recommendation is clear. Wherever possible (where unique valence structures can be drawn) obtain thermochemical data using *isodesmic* reactions, and then use these data for whatever purposes as needed.

References

1. W.J. Hehre, **Practical Strategies for Electronic Structure Calculations**, Wavefunction, Inc., Irvine, CA (1995).

Table 4-6: Heats of Formation from Bond Separation Reactions (kcal/mol)

molecule	bond separation reaction	6-31G*	MP2/6-31G*	pBP/DN*	expt.
ethylamine	$CH_3CH_2NH_2 + CH_4 \rightarrow CH_3CH_3 + CH_3NH_2$	-11	-12	-11	-11.4
dimethylamine	$CH_3NHCH_3 + NH_3 \rightarrow 2CH_3NH_2$	-2	-4	-3	-4.5
trimethylamine	$(CH_3)_3N + 2NH_3 \rightarrow 3CH_3NH_2$	0	-6	-2	-5.7
ethanol	$CH_3CH_2OH + CH_4 \rightarrow CH_3CH_3 + CH_3OH$	-54	-55	-55	-56.1
dimethyl ether	$CH_3OCH_3 + H_2O \rightarrow 2CH_3OH$	-41	-43	-42	-44.0
ethanethiol	$CH_3CH_2SH + CH_4 \rightarrow CH_3CH_3 + CH_3SH$	-9	-11	-10	-11.1
dimethyl sulfide	$CH_3SCH_3 + H_2S \rightarrow 2CH_3SH$	-7	-9	-8	-9.0
difluoromethane	$CH_2F_2 + CH_4 \rightarrow 2CH_3F$	-106	-108	-109	-106.8
trifluoromethane	$CHF_3 + 2CH_4 \rightarrow 3CH_3F$	-165	-170	-166	-164.5
tetrafluoromethane	$CF_4 + 3CH_4 \rightarrow 4CH_3F$	-225	-231	-219	-221
propene	$CH_3CH{=}CH_2 + CH_4 \rightarrow CH_3CH_3 + CH_2{=}CH_2$	6	5	5	4.8
acetaldehyde	$CH_3CHO + CH_4 \rightarrow CH_3CH_3 + H_2CO$	-40	-41	-40	-39.6
propyne	$CH_3C{\equiv}CH + CH_4 \rightarrow CH_3CH_3 + HC{\equiv}CH$	44	44	43	44.6
acetonitrile	$CH_3CN + CH_4 \rightarrow CH_3CH_3 + HCN$	18	19	17	15.4
formamide	$NH_2CHO + CH_4 \rightarrow CH_3NH_2 + H_2CO$	-46	-48	-48	-44.5
benzene	$\bigcirc + 6CH_4 \rightarrow 3CH_3CH_3 + 3CH_2{=}CH_2$	26	13	20	19.8
mean absolute error		2	2	2	-

114

Chapter 5

Representative Applications

This chapter provides a small selection of problems for which molecular mechanics calculations, semi-empirical and Hartree-Fock molecular orbital calculations, and MP2 and density functional correlated calculations are particularly well suited. In doing so, it illustrates a number of practical strategies for making effective use of different quantum chemical methods, as well as molecular mechanics methods, in order to achieve the desired results with the least effort.

Molecular mechanics models are restricted to the description of molecular equilibrium geometry and conformation. They are perhaps the only practical techniques for searching conformation space for any but the simplest molecules, and it is here that they have found greatest utility.

Semi-empirical models are particularly attractive for:

i) Equilibrium structure determinations for large molecules, where the cost of ***Hartree-Fock*** and ***MP2*** and ***density functional models*** may be prohibitive.

ii) Transition-state optimizations, where the cost of ***Hartree-Fock*** and ***MP2*** and ***density functional models*** may be prohibitive.

iii) Equilibrium and transition-state optimizations involving transition-metal inorganic and organometallic compounds, where ***Hartree-Fock models*** are known to produce poor results, and where the cost of ***MP2*** and ***density functional models*** may be prohibitive.

Semi-empirical models are unsuitable for :

i) Calculations on reaction energies, even the energies of *isodesmic* processes.

ii) Calculations of conformational energy differences.

Hartree-Fock models are particularly attractive for:

i) Structure determinations of medium-size organic and main-group inorganic molecules, where increased accuracy over that available from *semi-empirical models* is required, and where the cost of *MP2* and *density functional models* may be prohibitive.

ii) Calculations of reaction energies (except reactions involving net bond making or breaking), where *semi-empirical models* yield unacceptable results, and where the cost of *MP2* and *density functional models* may be prohibitive.

Hartree-Fock models are unsuitable for:

i) Calculation of reaction energies which involve net bond making or breaking and calculation of absolute activation energies.

ii) Structure determinations for transition-metal inorganic and organometallic molecules.

MP2 models and *density functional models* are needed for accurate descriptions of the thermochemistry of reactions which involve net bond making or breaking, and for calculation of absolute activation energies. Local *density functional models* do not provide acceptable results, but non-local models, such as the pBP model, provide good descriptions of reactions which involve net bond making or breaking. In practice, *MP2 models* may only be applied to relatively small molecules, whereas *density functional models* are comparable in cost to *Hartree-Fock models* for molecules of moderate size and less costly for large molecules.

Density functional models are particularly attractive for:

i) Calculations on large molecules, where the cost of *Hartree-Fock* and correlated *MP2 models* may be prohibitive, and where semi-empirical calculations may not be sufficiently accurate.

ii) Calculations on inorganic and organometallic systems where *Hartree-Fock models* may not be sufficiently accurate, and where the cost of *MP2 models* may be prohibitive.

iii) Thermochemical calculations, in particular, those which involve net bond making or breaking, and absolute activation energy calculations.

On the other hand, density functional models are not particularly well suited for :

i) Calculations on very small systems.

ii) Geometry and transition-state geometry optimization involving very "flat" potential energy surfaces.

The examples which follow illustrate how different models may be combined to rapidly solve the problem at hand, for example, *molecular mechanics models* to identify stable conformations and small-basis-set *Hartree-Fock models* or preferably *semi-empirical* models to obtain geometries (and transition-state geometries) in advance of energy (property) calculations with *MP2 models* or preferably *density functional models*. (A much more extensive series of examples may be found elsewhere.[1]) Most, if not all, of the examples provided involve relatively small molecules, and the strategies recommended to save time are not absolutely necessary. The point to be made is that for larger systems they may, in fact, be necessary.

---

1. W.J. Hehre, A.J. Shusterman and W.W. Huang, **A Laboratory Book of Computational Organic Chemistry**, Wavefunction, Inc., Irvine, CA, 1995.

Stabilizing Dewar Benzene[1]

Among the reasonable valence isomers of benzene, **1**, are Dewar benzene, **2**, prismane, **3**, benzvalene, **4**, and 3,3-bis (cyclopropene), **5**.

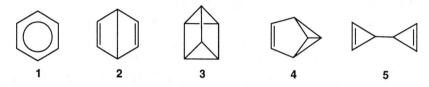

Dewar benzene has actually been isolated, and found to revert only slowly to benzene (its half life is approximately 2 days at 25°C). This is remarkable given how similar its geometry is to that of benzene, and what is expected to be a large thermodynamic driving force for the isomerization. The substituted Dewar benzene, **7**, formed from photolysis of 1,2,4-tri-*tert*-butylbenzene, **6**, reverts to its precursor only upon heating. Has the addition of the three bulky *tert*-butyl groups significantly affected (or even reversed) the relative thermochemical stabilities of the parent compounds?

$$\text{6} \quad \underset{\Delta}{\overset{h\nu}{\rightleftarrows}} \quad \text{7}$$

6   **7**

While benzene and Dewar benzene are small enough to be treated by the MP2 model, the corresponding tri-*tert*-butyl compounds are too large. The pBP/DN* density functional model should also be able to accurately account for relative energetics, and may easily be applied. It is important, however, to establish its performance (relative to MP2) on model systems where both are practical. It is also of interest to establish how closely the two models reproduce the estimated energy difference of 71 kcal/mol between benzene and Dewar benzene.[2]

    i)   Obtain equilibrium geometries for benzene and Dewar benzene using AM1 semi-empirical calculations, and use these for single energy calculations with both MP2/6-31G* and pBP/DN* models.

The two models provide nearly identical results (82 kcal/ mol in favor of benzene according to MP2/6-31G*//AM1, and 83 kcal/mol according to pBP/DN*//AM1) which are somewhat larger than the experimental estimate. The density functional model should be satisfactory in describing stability differences in substituted systems.

While geometry optimization on tri-*tert*-butyl benzene and its Dewar benzene analogue could easily be carried out using the pBP/DN* model, time could be saved by making use of AM1 equilibrium structures. In advance of this, it is important to assess the likely magnitude of errors introduced because of such a strategy.

ii) Optimize benzene and Dewar benzene using the pBP/DN* model. Compare relative energies with those obtained assuming AM1 equilibrium structures.

> *Using fully optimized geometries, the benzene/Dewar benzene energy difference in 81 kcal/mol compared to the previous result of 83 kcal/mol with AM1 geometries. An error of this magnitude is not large enough to alter any qualitative conclusions.*

iii) Optimize substituted forms of benzene and Dewar benzene using AM1, and follow these optimizations by single energy calculations using the pBP/DN* model.

> *The energy difference is reduced from 83 kcal/mol (in the parent compounds) to 41 kcal/mol in the tri-tert-butyl systems. The stabilities of the two compounds has not been reversed, and the energy of the substituted Dewar benzene relative to that of the substituted benzene is still too large to make its isolation simple.*

1. For a discussion see: F.A. Carey and R.J. Sundberg, **Advanced Organic Chemsitry**, 3rd Ed., Part A, Plenum Press, New York, 1990, p.604.
2. M.J. Goldstein and R.S. Leight, *J. Am. Chem. Soc.*, **99**, 8112 (1977).

Protonation of Lysine

Where does the amino acid lysine protonate, on the nitrogen directly attached to the α carbon or the one at the end of the sidechain? To find out, the energies of both protonated structures need to be calculated. The situation is further complicated by the fact that lysine and its protonated forms are flexible molecules. At the very least, the lowest-energy conformer needs to be located for each. A more rigorous approach (not considered here) would be to identify all low energy conformers for all three molecules, and then to use the Boltzmann equation to establish average energies.

i) Perform conformational searches using MMFF94 molecular mechanics on the non-zwitterionic form of lysine*, and on its two nitrogen-protonated forms. Next, perform semi-empirical AM1 geometry optimizations, and then Hartree-Fock 6-31G* single energy calculations on the global minimum, and additionally on all conformers that are within 5 kcal/mol of the global minimum for each system (according to the MMFF94 mechanics calculations). Identify the lowest-energy conformer for each, and assign the more stable protonated structure. Calculate the proton affinity of lysine based on the more stable protonated structure (the energy of proton is 0 hartrees). How does it compare with the experimental proton affinity of 229 kcal/mol?

The lowest-energy conformers of lysine (left) and its α N-protonated (middle) and sidechain N-protonated (right) forms are as follows:

Protonation occurs on the sidechain nitrogen and the proton affinity of lysine is 245 kcal/mol.

---

* In the gas phase, lysine is more stable in the non-zwitterionic form ($H_2N–CHR–CO_2H$) than in the zwitterionic form ($H_3N^+–CHR–CO_2^-$) found in water.

An absolute proton affinity corresponds to the energy of a reaction in which a nonbonded electron pair is replaced by a bond. The energy for this type of reaction is difficult to obtain accurately using simple models (such as the Hartree-Fock 6-31G* model). However, the energy of the *isodesmic* reaction comparing the proton affinity of lysine to that of methylamine as a standard, i.e.

protonated lysine + methylamine → lysine + protonated methylamine

should be well described at this level of calculation. Combined with the experimental proton affinity of methylamine, this should give a better estimate of the proton affinity of lysine.

ii) Perform AM1 geometry optimizations on methylamine and protonated methylamine, and follow these with single energy 6-31G* Hartree-Fock calculations. Work out the energy of the *isodesmic* reaction above, and add this energy to the experimental proton affinity of methylamine (214 kcal/mol).

> *The proton affinity of lysine is 14 kcal/mol greater than that of methylamine. A better estimate of the absolute proton affinity of lysine is 228 kcal/mol. This is in good accord with the experimental proton affinity of lysine (229 kcal/mol).*

Stable Carbenes

Carbenes are only rarely detected, let alone isolated and characterized. Kinetically favorable exothermic reactions (among them cycloaddition with alkenes and insertion into CH bonds) generally preclude this. 1,3-Diadamantylimidazol-2-ylidene, **1Ad**, is an exception in that it forms a stable solid, the structure of which has been determined.[1]

1Ad   **1Me**   **2**

Is the stability of **1Ad** due to unfavorable kinetics, i.e., the bulky admantyl groups blocking reaction, or to unfavorable thermochemistry, i.e., loss of aromaticity of the imidazole ring as a result of reaction? To decide, compare the kinetics and thermodynamics of the insertion of **1Ad** into the central CH bond in propane with reactions of **1Me**, which should also be "aromatic" but lacks "shielding groups", and **2**, which is neither aromatic nor crowded. While **1Me**, **2** and their insertion transition states and products are small enough to easily be treated using the MP2 model, **1Ad** is close to practical limits. The pBP/DN* model is practical, although it is important to establish its performance (relative to MP2) on suitable model compounds.

i)   Obtain geometries for **2**, its CH insertion transition-state and insertion product using semi-empirical AM1 calculations. Perform single energy calculations with both MP2/6-31G* and pBP/DN* models.

> *Both the energy barrier (9 kcal/mol) and overall reaction exothermicity (71 kcal/mol) obtained from pBP/DN* calculations are similar to the corresponding values obtained from MP2/6-31G* calculations (10 and 89 kcal/mol, respectively). Both portray a highly exothermic process with a small activation energy. The pBP/DN**

*model should be able to adequately account for the kinetics and thermodynamics of reactions of **1Ad** and **1Me**.*

Use of AM1 geometries provides enormous cost savings for calculations involving **1Ad** and **1Me**. It is important to assess the likely error resulting from such a strategy for reactions involving **2**, where geometries from the pBP/DN* model may easily be obtained.

ii) Optimize propane, dichlorocarbene and the transition-state and product of dichlorocarbene insertion into the central CH bond in propane using the pBP/DN* model. Compare the energy barrier and the overall thermodynamics of the insertion reaction with those obtained previously assuming AM1 geometries.

> *Using fully optimized geometries, the activation barrier for dichlorocarbene insertion into propane is 7 kcal/mol and the process is exothermic by 68 kcal/mol. These are very close to values of 9 kcal/mol and 71 kcal/mol obtained from use of AM1 geometries.*

iii) Obtain equilibrium geometries for **1Ad** and **1Me**, and for the two products following insertion into the central CH bond in propane. Similarly, locate the AM1 transition states for insertion into **1Ad** and **1Me**. Use the resulting structures for single energy calculations with the pBP/DN* model.

> *Energy barriers for CH insertion of **1Ad** and **1Me** are 78 and 56 kcal/mol, respectively. Reaction of **1Me** with propane is exothermic by 5 kcal/mol, while the corresponding reaction of **1Ad** is endothermic by 18 kcal/mol. These contrast with the activation barrier and exothermicity for reaction of **2** with propane (9 and 10 kcal/mol, respectively), suggesting loss of aromatic stability of **1Ad** and **1Me** as a result of reaction. The difference in activation barriers and exothermicities for reactions of **1Ad** and **1Me** (22 and 23 kcal/mol, respectively) reflects steric differences.*

---

1.   A.J. Arduengo, III, R.L. Harlow and M. Kline, *J. Am. Chem. Soc.*, **113**, 361 (1991).

Thermodynamic vs. Kinetic Control in Radical Cyclizations

Cyclization of hex-5-enyl radical, **1**, can either yield cyclopentylmethyl radical, **2**, or cyclohexyl radical, **3**.

While **3** might be expected to be more stable than **2** (**3** should be less strained than **2**, and 2° radicals are generally more stable than 1° radicals), products formed from cyclopentylmethyl radicals usually dominate, e.g.

Calculations can be employed to establish the identity of both the most stable and most rapidly formed radical intermediate, and so to decide whether the observed preference is kinetic or thermodynamic.

i) Obtain equilibrium geometries for cyclopentylmethyl radical, **2**, and cyclohexyl radical, **3**, using the AM1 semi-empirical model. Follow these with single MP2/6-31G* energy calculations.

> *MP2/6-31G*//AM1 calculations show that cyclohexyl radical is 10 kcal/mol more stable than cyclopentylmethyl radical. This is not unexpected (see above). The difference in energies (10 kcal/mol) is large enough such that products derived from cyclopentylmethyl radical would not be observed were the reaction under thermodynamic control. As products from cyclopentylmethyl radical **are observed**, and in fact dominate the product mixture, the calculations suggest that the cyclization reaction is not under thermodynamic control.*

ii) Obtain AM1 transition-state structures for hex-5-enyl radical, **1**, rearranging to cyclopentylmethyl radical, **2**, and to cyclohexyl radical, **3**. Follow these with single MP2/6-31G* energy calculations.

> *MP2/6-31G*//AM1 calculations show that formation of cyclopentylmethyl radical from 1 occurs with an activation energy which is 2 kcal/mol lower than that required for formation of cyclohexyl radical. This corresponds to a ratio of 5-membered ring products of approximately 95:5 at room temperature.*

The calculated energy differences (especially the difference in barrier heights) are small and may be sensitive to the use of approximate AM1 geometries. While these systems are too large for complete structure (and transition-structure) optimizations using the MP2/6-31G* model, they are easily ammenable to calculations using the Hartree-Fock 3-21G model.

iii) Repeat the above thermochemical and barrier height calculations using Hartree-Fock 3-21G equilibrium and transition-state geometries in place of semi-empirical AM1 geometries.

> *MP2/6-31G*//3-21G calculations show that cyclohexyl radical is 7 kcal/mol more stable than cyclopentylmethyl radical, but is more difficult to form from 1 (by 3 kcal/ mol). These results are in close accord with those obtained using AM1 geometries.*

> *Overall, the calculations support the idea that ring cyclization is under kinetic and not thermodynamic control.*

Effect of Conformation on Rates of Diels-Alder Reactions

The conformations of conjugated dienes, such as 1,3-butadiene, are governed by a combination of electronic and steric interactions. The preferred *trans* arrangement minimizes steric interactions while allowing the two π bonds to be coplanar and maximize conjugation. The geometry of the higher-energy *"cis"* conformer is now known not to be perfectly planar, so as to maximize conjugation, but rather is slightly twisted, in order to relieve steric crowding.

Is the *trans* preference in 1,3-butadiene responsible for the fact that the barrier for Diels-Alder cycloaddition of 1,3-butadiene and acrylonitrile has been estimated to be approximately 10 kcal/mol higher than the barrier for cycloaddition of cyclopentadiene and acrylonitrile?[1] Cyclopentadiene is "locked" into a *cis* conformation, and the extra energy required for butadiene addition might be due in whole or part to *"cis"-trans* energy difference. Of course, there is an alternative explanation. Cyclopentadiene is more "electron rich" than 1,3-butadiene due to the methylene group connecting terminal carbons.

Calculations can estimate both the energy difference between *trans* and *"cis"* 1,3-butadiene, and the difference in activation energies for Diels-Alder cycloadditions of 1,3-butadiene and cyclopentadiene with acrylonitrile. This should shed light on the difference in Diels-Alder reactivities of the two dienes.

i) Obtain equilibrium geometries for *"cis"* and *trans* conformers of 1,3-butadiene using AM1 semi-empirical calculations, and follow these with single energy calculations using the MP2/6-31G* model.

   MP2/6-31G//AM1 calculations show that "cis" - 1,3-butadiene is 3 kcal/mol higher in energy than trans-1,3-butadiene. (The actual AM1 dihedral angle is approximately 40°, meaning that the "reactive" conformer of 1,3-butadiene is far from planar.)*

ii) Obtain AM1 equilibrium geometries for acrylonitrile and cyclopentadiene, and follow these with MP2/6-31G* energy calculations. Obtain AM1 transition-state geometries for reactions of *"cis"*-1,3-butadiene and acrylonitrile and of cyclopentadiene and acrylonitrile. Perform single MP2/6-31G* energy calculations on the two transition structures.

> *MP2/6-31G*//AM1 calculations show activation energy barriers for the cycloadditions involving "cis"-1,3-butadiene and cyclopentadiene of 11 and 7 kcal/mol respectively. The difference (4 kcal/mol in favor of addition of cyclopentadiene) is only slightly greater than the "cis"-trans energy difference in 1,3-butadiene. Note, however, that the calculated difference in activation energies for Diels-Alder reactions involving 1,3-butadiene and cyclopentadiene is significantly lower than the previous estimate of 10 kcal/mol.[1]*

These energy differences are quite small and could be sensitive to the choice of geometries. MP2/6-31G* geometry (transition-state geometry) optimizations are too costly to consider, but the Hartree-Fock 3-21G model may easily be applied to this task.

iii) Repeat the calculations using Hartree-Fock 3-21G equilibrium and transition-state geometries in place of semi-empirical AM1 structures.

> *MP2/6-31G*//3-21G calculations show "cis"-trans energy differences in 1,3-butadiene of 3 kcal/mol, unchanged from the value obtained using AM1 geometries. Activation barriers calculated at this level are 10 and 6 kcal/mol for additions involving "cis"-1,3-butadiene and cyclopentadiene, respectively, again nearly identical to the earlier results.*
>
> *Overall, it appears that the difference in energies between "cis" and trans conformers of 1,3-butadiene accounts in large part for the fact that the barrier for Diels-Alder cycloaddition of 1,3-butadiene and acrylonitrile is higher than that for the corresponding reaction involving cyclopentadiene.*

---

1. K.N. Houk, *Pure and Appl. Chem.*, **61**, 643 (1989).

Chapter 6

Graphical Models

This chapter introduces isosurface displays of molecular orbitals, electron densities, spin densities and electrostatic potentials, and relates them to molecular size and shape and charge distribution. It also introduces and illustrates "property maps" which simultaneously depict both size and shape and a molecular property.

Among the quantities which have proven to be of importance as graphical models are the molecular orbitals, the electron density, the spin density (for radicals and other molecules with unpaired electrons) and the electrostatic potential. These may all be expressed as three-dimensional functions of the coordinates. To display them on a two-dimensional video screen, it is necessary to define a surface of constant value, a so-called **isovalue surface** or, more simply, **isosurface**[*], i.e.

$$f(x,y,z) = constant \qquad (1)$$

While the value of the constant is arbitrary, it may be chosen to reflect a particular physical observable of interest, e.g., the "electronic size" of a molecule in the case of display of electron density.

Graphical models are not restricted to isosurfaces. It is possible to present additional information in terms of a **property map** on top of an isosurface, where different colors may be used to portray different property values. Most common are maps on top of an electron density surface. Here the surface designates overall molecular size and shape, and the map represents the value of some property at various points on the surface. For example, the value of the electrostatic potential (the energy of interaction of a positive point charge with the nuclei

---

[*] Another common display technique is to define a two-dimensional plane or "slice" which cuts into the overall three-dimensional function, and to demark equal value lines (contours) onto this slice. Both isosurface and slice displays are available in SPARTAN.

129

and electrons of a molecule) mapped onto an electron density isosurface may be employed to distinguish regions on the surface which are electron rich (subject to electrophilic attack) from those which are electron poor (subject to nucleophilic attack).

This chapter introduces isosurface displays of molecular orbitals, electron and spin densities and electrostatic potentials, as well as maps of key molecular orbitals and electrostatic potentials on top of electron density surfaces. It illustrates the utility of both isosurfaces and maps with regard to the description of molecular structure and stability and chemical reactivity and selectivity. Further applications of graphical models are considered in the next chapter.

Molecular Orbitals

Chemists are very familiar with the molecular orbitals of simple molecules. They easily recognize the σ and π orbitals of ethyne, and without difficulty associate these with the molecule's σ and π bonds.

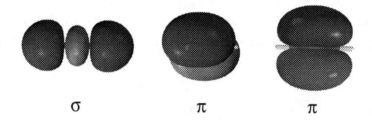

$$\sigma \qquad \pi \qquad \pi$$

Note, however, that even in such a simple case as this, molecular orbitals do not necessarily correspond one-to-one with bonds. For example, the highest-energy σ orbital in ethyne is clearly made up of both CC and CH bonding components. This may be rationalized by recognizing that molecular orbitals, $\psi(\mathbf{r})$, are written as linear combinations of nuclear-centered basis function, $\phi(\mathbf{r})$, and as such are completely delocalized.

$$\psi_i(\mathbf{r}) = \sum_{\mu}^{\text{basis functions}} c_{\mu i}\phi_\mu(\mathbf{r}) \qquad (2)$$

Ever since the pioneering work of Woodward and Hoffmann[1], chemists have recognized that the nodal structure of the valence molecular orbital manifold is key to understanding why some chemical reactions proceed easily whereas others do not. For example, the fact that the highest-occupied molecular orbital (**HOMO**) in *cis*-1,3-butadiene is able to interact favorably with the lowest-unoccupied molecular orbital (**LUMO**) in ethene, suggests that the two molecules should be able to combine in a concerted manner to form cyclohexene.

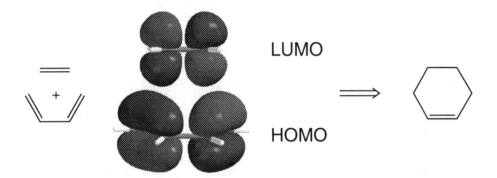

On the other hand, interaction between the HOMO on one ethene and the LUMO on another ethene is not favorable, and concerted addition to form cyclobutane would not be expected.

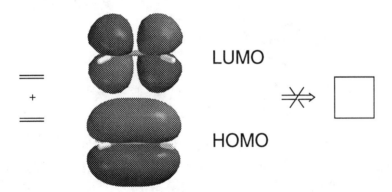

"Orbital symmetry arguments" are not commonly extended beyond planar π systems. In great part, this is due to the difficulty of constructing and "sketching" by hand and visualizing molecular orbitals of three-dimensional systems, a situation which modern computer graphics has now completely altered.

Molecular orbitals do not need to be directly involved in bonding to be informative. For example, the highest-occupied molecular orbital of sulfur tetrafluoride clearly reveals that the molecule incorporates a lone pair on sulfur, in accord with a classical valence structure.*

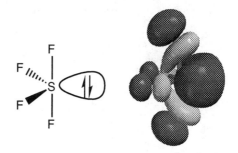

Molecular orbital descriptions may often be related to "conventional" chemical indicators, and as such may be useful in interpreting molecular properties and chemical reactivities. For example, the LUMO of planar (top) and perpendicular (bottom) benzyl cation anticipate the difference in charge delocalization of the two systems.

It is into the LUMO, the energetically most accessible unfilled molecular orbital, that any further electrons will go. Hence, it may be thought of as demarking the location of positive charge in a molecule. The LUMO in planar benzyl cation is delocalized away from the formal cation center and onto the *ortho* and *para* ring carbons, in accord with classical resonance structures. On the other hand, the LUMO in perpendicular benzyl cation is primarily localized on the benzylic carbon, in accord with the classical resonance picture. "Chemical intuition" suggests that delocalization of the positive charge leads to stabilization. Thus, planar benzyl cation is more stable

---

* This is, of course why SF_4 adopts a trigonal bipyramidal as opposed to a tetrahedral equilibrium geometry.

than perpendicular benzyl cation.

Molecular orbital descriptions offer a number of significant advantages over conventional Lewis structures. For one, they often provide "more compact" descriptions than Lewis structures. Second, orbital descriptions are quantitative compared to the strictly qualitative nature of Lewis structures. Finally, molecular orbital descriptions may be applied much more widely than Lewis descriptions.

Electron Densities

The total electron density, or more simply, the electron density, $\rho(\mathbf{r})$, is a function of the coordinates $\mathbf{r}$, defined such that $\rho(\mathbf{r})d\mathbf{r}$ is the number of electrons inside a small volume $d\mathbf{r}$. This is what is measured in an X-ray diffraction experiment. For a (closed-shell) molecule, $\rho(\mathbf{r})$ is written in terms of a sum of products of basis functions.

$$\rho(\mathbf{r}) = \sum_{\mu\nu}^{\text{basis functions}} P_{\mu\nu}\phi_\mu(\mathbf{r})\phi_\nu(\mathbf{r}) \tag{3}$$

Here, the ϕ are basis functions and P is the so-called density matrix. The electron density may be portrayed in terms of an isosurface, an **isodensity surface**, with the size and shape of the surface being given by the value of the density.

← large density value

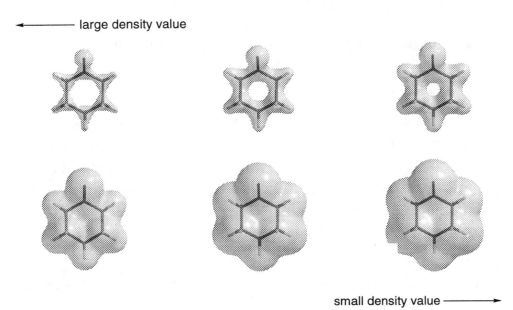

small density value →

133

Depending on this value, isodensity surfaces may either serve to locate chemical bonds, or to indicate overall molecular size and shape. For example, a 0.1 electrons/au^3 isodensity surface for cyclohexanone conveys very much the same information as a conventional skeletal structure model, that is, it depicts the locations of bonds.

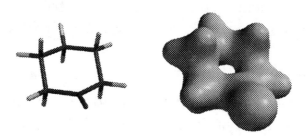

A different isdensity surface (0.002 electrons/au^3) serves to portray overall molecular size and shape. This is, of course, the same information portrayed by a conventional space-filling (CPK) model.*

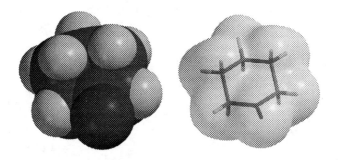

In the discussions which follow, a 0.1 electrons/bohr^3 isodensity surface will be referred to as a **bond surface** and a 0.002 electrons/bohr^3 isodensity surface as a **size surface**.

Calculated isodensity surfaces offer some significant advantages over conventional skeletal and space-filling models. Most important, isodensity surfaces may be applied to elucidate chemical bonding and not only to portray "known" bonding. For example, a bond surface for diborane clearly shows a molecule with very little electron density concentrated between the two borons.

---

* The radii used to define CPK models have been chosen to reflect the space which molecules take up when they pack in solids (or associate in liquids).

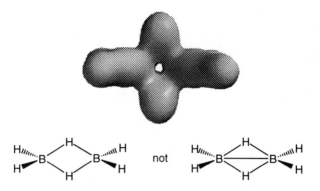

The appropriate structure model is then one which lacks a boron-boron bond, rather than one which shows the two borons to be directly bonded.

By far the most interesting and most important application of bond surfaces is to the description of transition states for chemical reactions. They are able to clearly discern which bonds are being broken and which are being formed. An example is the pyrolysis of ethyl formate, leading to formic acid and ethene.

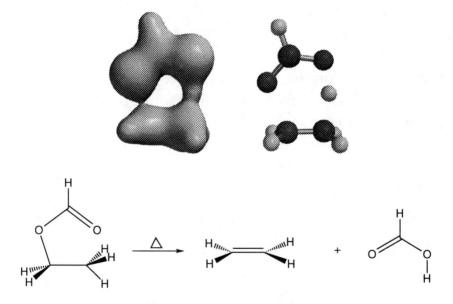

The bond surface offers clear evidence of a "late transition state". The CO bond is nearly fully cleaved and the migrating hydrogen seems more tightly bound to oxygen (as in the product) than to carbon (as in the reactant). Further information, in particular, about the timing of the overall reaction, may be obtained by replacing the static picture above by a "movie", i.e., animation along the reaction coordinate.* Because direct information about the structure and bonding of transition states is unavailable from experiment,** the models here are potentially of much greater value than they are for "normal" (stable) molecules.

The second significant advantage offered by isodensity surfaces over conventional structure models is that they are quantitative. They can be used to uncover trends in bonding, and thereby help in development of qualitative descriptions. For example, size surfaces for the isoelectronic molecules, methyl anion (left), ammonia (middle) and hydronium cation (right) clearly show a decrease in overall size with increasing nuclear charge.

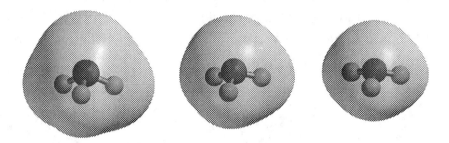

They support the notion that molecules are held together by Coulombic attraction between nuclei and electrons, and that the greater the nuclear charge (for a given number of electrons) the more tightly will the electrons be held.

Spin Densities

The spin density, $\rho^{spin}(\mathbf{r})$, is defined as the difference in electron density formed by electrons of α spin, $\rho^{\alpha}(\mathbf{r})$, and the electron density formed by electrons of β spin, $\rho^{\beta}(\mathbf{r})$.

$$\rho^{spin}(\mathbf{r}) = \rho^{\alpha}(\mathbf{r}) - \rho^{\beta}(\mathbf{r}) = \sum_{\mu\nu}^{\text{basis functions}} (P_{\mu\nu}^{\alpha} - P_{\mu\nu}^{\beta}) \, \phi_{\mu}(\mathbf{r})\phi_{\nu}(\mathbf{r}) \qquad (4)$$

---

* SPARTAN allows animated display of isosurfaces and property maps (see discussion following) along a reaction coordinate.

** Of course, some insight may be gained about transition-state structure from such quantities as activation entropies and activation volumes as well as kinetic isotope effects.

Here, the ϕ are basis functions and P^{α} and P^{β} are the α and β density matrices, respectively.

For closed-shell (electron-paired) molecules, the spin density is zero everywhere. For open-shell molecules, the spin density indicates the distribution of unpaired electrons. Spin density is an obvious indicator of reactivity for free radicals; bonds will be made to centers for which the spin is greatest. For example, the spin density isosurface for allyl radical suggests that reaction will occur on one of the terminal carbons and not on the central carbon.

This is what is observed and, of course, is also anticipated using conventional resonance structures.

Spin density isosurfaces offer some significant advantages over conventional resonance structures insofar as anticipating structure and reactivity. For one, while resonance structures are relatively easy to construct for simple "planar" systems (such as allyl radical), and their interpretation relatively straightforward, there is much less experience in applying resonance arguments to larger ("three-dimensional") systems. Additionally, resonance arguments are completely inadequate for discussions of subtle differences which are often critical in dictating structure, stability and reactivity, for example, differences caused by remote substituents effects of by changes in stereochemistry. In these situations, spin density isosurfaces are able to provide a quantitative account.

For doublet states (free radicals) the distribution of spin (as defined above) is usually properly represented by the highest-occupied molecular orbital of α spin (ignoring the sign of the orbital). This simply reflects the idealized situation in which all electrons except that occupying the highest-energy molecular orbital of α spin are paired.

Electrostatic Potentials

The electrostatic potential, ε_p, is defined as the energy of interaction of a positive point charge located at p with the nuclei and electrons of a molecule.

$$\varepsilon_p = \overset{\text{nuclei}}{\underset{A}{\sum}} \frac{Z_A}{R_{Ap}} - \overset{\text{basis functions}}{\underset{\mu\nu}{\sum}} P_{\mu\nu} \int \frac{\phi_\mu^*(\mathbf{r})\phi_\nu(\mathbf{r})}{r_{rp}} \, d\mathbf{r} \qquad (5)$$

The first summation is over nuclei A; Z are atomic numbers and R are distances between the nuclei and the point charge. The second pair of summations is over basis functions, ϕ; P is the density matrix, and the integrals reflect Coulombic interactions between the electrons and the point charge, where r is the distance separating the electron and the point charge.

An isosurface for which the electrostatic potential is negative (a negative **isopotential surface**) delineates regions in a molecule which are subject to electrophilic attack, for example, above and below the plane of the ring in benzene (left) and in the ring plane in pyridine (right).

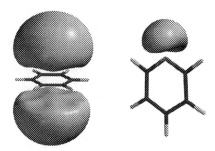

While these two molecules are structurally very similar, isopotential surfaces make clear that this similarity does not carry over into electrophilic reactivity.

More generally, isopotential surfaces serve to "outline" the location of the highest-energy electrons. For example, negative isopotential surfaces for trimethylamine (left), dimethyl ether (middle) and fluoromethane (right) are an artifact of the nonbonded "lone pairs" of electrons.

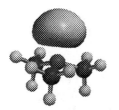

While the first of these results from a single nonbonded valence molecular orbital (the highest-occupied molecular orbital), the electrostatic potential in dimethyl ether and fluoromethane result from a combination of two and three high-lying nonbonded molecular orbitals, respectively.

It might be thought that isosurfaces for which the electrostatic potential is positive should, in a similar way, demark particularly electron-poor regions of a molecule, and thus serve as indicators of nucleophilic reactivity. In practice, however, they have not proven to be particularly valuable, although, positive regions of electrostatic potential maps (to be discussed later in this chapter) have found utility in this regard.

Property Maps

Additional information (a "property") may be added to any isosurface by using color to represent the value of the property. Colors at one end of the visible spectrum could represent "small" property values and at the other end, "large" property values. This gives rise to a model which actually conveys four dimensions on information.[*]

$$
\begin{array}{rl}
3 & \text{dimensions conveying structure} \\
+\,1 & \text{dimension conveying property value} \\
\hline
4 & \text{dimensions}
\end{array}
$$

The most commonly used isosurface onto which to map a property is the 0.002 electrons/au^3 electron density isosurface (the size surface). This depicts overall molecular size and shape and therefore surface regions "visible" to an incoming reagent.[**]

---

[*]   Actually, it is possible to simultaneously map the values of two different properties on an isosurface, leading to a representation which conveys five dimensions of information (three dimensions conveying structure and two dimensions conveying two different properties).

[**]   This is not necessarily the same as depicting regions which are **accessible** to an incoming reagent.

To see how property maps are constructed, first consider both a size surface and a (negative) isopotential surface for benzene.

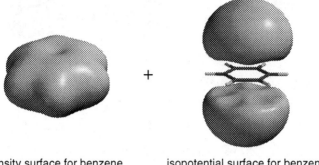

isodensity surface for benzene   isopotential surface for benzene

Both of these surfaces convey structure. The density surface reveals the size and shape of benzene, while the isopotential surface delineates in which regions surrounding benzene a particular (negative) electrostatic potential will be felt.

Next, consider making a "map" of the value of the electrostatic potential on the electron density surface, using colors to designate values of the potential. This leaves the isodensity surface unchanged (insofar as representing the size and shape of benzene), but replaces the grayscale image (conveying only structural information) into a color image (conveying the value of the electrostatic potential *in addition to* structure).

electrostatic potential map for benzene

In this case, colors near red represent large negative values of the potential, while colors near blue represent large positive values (orange, yellow and green represent intermediate values of the potential). Note that the π system is "red", consistent with the (negative) isopotential surface previously shown.

Property maps have found a myriad of uses. Especially useful is an **electrostatic potential map**, a map of the electrostatic potential on the electron density (size surface). This simultaneously conveys molecular size and shape and overall charge distribution. For example, an electrostatic potential map of the zwitterionic form of β-alanine ($^+H_3NCH_2CH_2CO_2^-$) shows, as expected, positive charge (blue color) in the vicinity of protonated amine, negative charge (red color) in the vicinity of the deprotonated carboxylic acid and a central region which is "neutral" (green color).

Another good example involves comparison of electrostatic potential maps for planar (top) and perpendicular (bottom) conformers of benzyl cation.

The latter reveals heavy concentration of positive charge (blue color) on the benzylic carbon and perpendicular to the plane of the ring.

This is consistent both with the familiar resonance picture of the ion for which only a single structure may be drawn, as well as with the fact that the LUMO is localized almost entirely on the benzylic carbon (see previous discussion). On the other hand, planar benzyl cation shows no such buildup of positive charge on the benzylic carbon, but rather delocalization onto *ortho* and *para* ring carbons, exactly as suggested by resonance theory, and by the LUMO which is delocalized over four centers.

Electrostatic potential maps may also be employed to characterize transition states in chemical reactions. A good example is pyrolysis of ethyl formate (leading to formic acid and ethene).

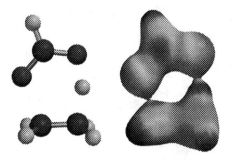

Here, an electrostatic potential map clearly shows that the hydrogen being transferred (from carbon to oxygen) is positively charged (it is an electrophile).

The electrostatic potential is not the only useful quantity that can be mapped on the electron density. Maps of certain key molecular orbitals may also lead to informative models. Consider, for example, a **LUMO map**, that is, a map of the (absolute) value of the lowest-unoccupied molecular orbital in cyclohexenone.

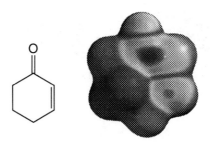

Recall that the LUMO delineates areas which are most electron deficient, hence subject to nucleophilic attack. One of these areas in cyclohexenone is clearly the carbonyl carbon, consistent with the observation that carbonyl compounds undergo nucleophilic addition at the carbonyl carbon. The other area is the β carbon, again consistent with the known chemistry of α,β-unsaturated carbonyl compounds, in this case Michael addition.

$$\underset{\text{carbonyl addition}}{\overset{\text{CH}_3\text{Li}}{\longleftarrow}} \qquad \underset{\text{Michael addition}}{\overset{(\text{CH}_3)_2\text{CuLi}}{\longrightarrow}}$$

While the buildup of positive charge on the β carbon leading to possibility of Michael addition could have been easily anticipated from resonance arguments, i.e.,

resonance arguments could not easily account for changes in nucleophilic reactivity as a result of substitution on the ring, for example, methyl substitution on α the and β carbons. Here the LUMO maps provide clear results, suggesting that substitution on the α carbon has little overall effect, whereas analogous β substitution significantly enhances reactivity at the carbonyl carbon.

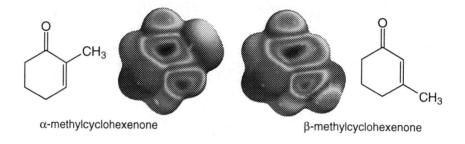

α-methylcyclohexenone   β-methylcyclohexenone

Practical Considerations

Semi-empirical models generally provide reasonable qualitative descriptions of the sizes and shapes of molecular orbitals, electron densities, spin densities and electrostatic potentials. They can, for example, be employed to establish the symmetries of key molecular orbitals or to assess bonding in transition states. Such models are, however, not as successful in describing subtle changes in size and shape in response to subtle changes in chemical structure or molecular environment. On the other hand, Hartree-Fock models have proven to be generally satisfactory, although split-valence or polarization basis sets are required. Limited experience suggests that correlated (MP2 and density functional) models also provide a satisfactory basis for graphical analyses, although there is little evidence to suggest that they provide better descriptions than Hartree-Fock models. Except where cost considerations might weigh in their favor, i.e., with density functional models, there is little to recommend the use of correlated models for this purpose.

1. R.B. Woodward and R. Hoffmann, **The Conservation of Orbital Symmetry**, Verlag Chemie GmbH, Weinheim, 1970.

Chapter 7

Application of Graphical Models

This chapter illustrates applications of graphical models to the investigation of molecular interactions and to the description of chemical reactivity and selectivity.

While it is common to think of molecular modeling in terms of quantitative calculations of molecular structures and energies, this is but one aspect of the subject. Another, quite different, perspective follows from application of the types of graphical models described in the preceeding chapter. Molecular orbitals, electron densities, spin densities and electrostatic potentials, obtained from quantum chemical methods, may be employed to provide fundamental insights into the structures and stabilities of molecules, as well as the way molecules interact with one another and react.

This chapter presents a series of problems for which the use of graphical models is particularly appropriate. These have been drawn from recently published compilations of computational organic "experiments"[1,2], and the reader is directed to the sources for additional examples.

1. W.J. Hehre, A.J. Shusterman and W.W. Huang, **A Laboratory Book of Computational Organic Chemistry**, Wavefunction, Inc., Irvine, CA, 1995.
2. W.J. Hehre, A.J. Shusterman and J.E. Nelson, **The Molecular Modeling Workbook for Organic Chemistry**, Wavefunction, Inc., Irvine, CA, 1998.

Structure of Benzene in the Solid State

The structure of the guanine-cytosine base pair is familiar to all chemists and is easily rationalized in terms of hydrogen bonding.

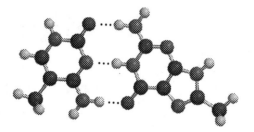

An alternative view is provided by a pair of electrostatic potential maps. Electron-rich heteroatoms line up with the electron-poor (acidic) hydrogens. Attraction between the two bases is, therefore, due to Coulombic interactions.

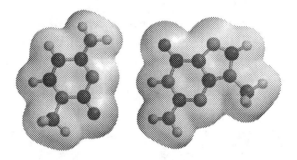

What would be the geometry of the guanine-cytosine complex were there no hydrogen bonds or, more to the point, were chemists not to know about the "benefits" of hydrogen bonding? More than likely, this would be a more closely-packed geometry, such as the following.

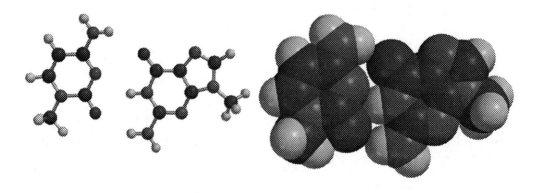

The question is relevant because there are numerous situations where electrostatic interactions may not be "obvious", but may still be very important in directing intermolecular geometry. Without explicit knowledge, the obvious thing to do will be to associate molecules as tightly as steric dictates will permit.

As a case in point, consider the structure of benzene in the solid state.[1] Does it assume a geometry in which the rings are "stacked", or a structure in which the rings are perpendicular (or nearly perpendicular) to one another?

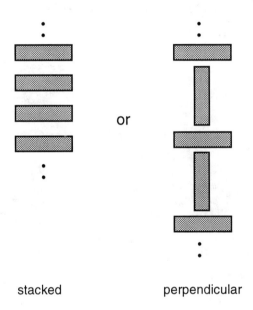

stacked   perpendicular

Most chemists would "guess" the former. Graphical models can show why the perpendicular structure is actually favored.

i)   Obtain and examine an electrostatic potential map for benzene using 3-21G Hartree-Fock calculations.

> *The electrostatic potential map for benzene clearly shows that the π face is electron rich (red color) and the periphery is electron poor (blue color), consistent with the usual notion that π electrons are "more available" than σ electrons.*

This suggests that stacking the rings would result in unfavorable electrostatic interactions, while a perpendicular arrangement of benzene rings would result in favorable electrostatic interactions between the π and σ systems.

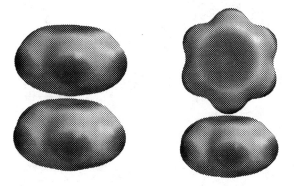

ii)   To confirm (or refute) the conclusions of the graphical models, optimize benzene and both "stacked" and perpendicular dimers using 3-21G Hartree-Fock calculations, and determine the dimerization energy for each.

According to 3-21G calculations, the perpendicular dimer with a hydrogen to ring distance of 2.84Å is 1.1 kcal/mol more stable than two benzenes, while the "stacked" dimer actually dissociates according to the calculations.

1. E.G. Cox, D.W.J. Cruickshank and J.A.S. Smith, *Proc. Roy. Soc.*, **A247**, 1 (1958).

Acidities of Carboxylic Acids

It has long been known that the acidity of a substituted benzoic acid is often closely correlated with the reaction rate of an identically-substituted aromatic compound. For example, pK_a's of carboxylic acids are correlated with hydrolysis rates of their methyl esters. For this reason, pK_a values often provide useful insight into chemical reactivity.

While pK_a's can be directly calculated, i.e., in terms of the energy of deprotonation of their neutral acids, it is useful to explore to what extent electrostatic potential maps are able to uncover trends in acidities. For example, are they able to reveal that the acidic hydrogen in a strong acid, such as nitric acid, is more positive than that in a weak acid, such as acetic acid, which in turn is more positive than that in a very weak acid, such as ethanol?

i)   Obtain equilibrium geometries for nitric acid, acetic acid and ethanol using semi-empirical AM1 calculations. Follow these by single energy calculations using the Hartree-Fock 6-31G** model. For each, calculate an electrostatic potential map, and compare the maps with specific focus on the region around the "acidic hydrogen".

> *The maximum (most positive) electrostatic potentials (in the vicinity of the acidic hydrogen) are: 99 kcal/mol (nitric acid); 64 kcal/mol (acetic acid); 58 kcal/mol (ethanol). These data suggest that acid strength and electrostatic potential on the acidic hydrogen are related and, given this, that the calculations parallel the known ordering of acid strengths in these compounds.*

Are the calculations able to account for subtle changes in acid strengths among related compounds, for example, changes in the acidities of carboxylic acids with change in structure?

ii)   Obtain equilibrium geometries for the carboxylic acids tabulated below using the AM1 model, and follow these with single energy calculations using Hartree-Fock 6-31G** calculations. For each, calculate an electrostatic potential map, and compare the maps with specific focus on the region around the acidic hydrogen. Plot maximum electrostatic potential vs. aqueous pK_a (given below).

acid	pK_a^1	acid	pK_a^1
Cl_3C-CO_2H	0.7	$H-CO_2H$	3.75
HO_2C-CO_2H	1.23	*trans*-$ClCH=CH-CO_2H$	3.79
Cl_2CH-CO_2H	1.48	$C_6H_5-CO_2H$	4.19
$NCCH_2-CO_2H$	2.45	*para*–$ClC_6H_4-CH=CHCO_2H$	4.41
$ClCH_2-CO_2H$	2.85	*trans*–$CH_3CH=CH-CO_2H$	4.70
trans-$HO_2CCH=CH-CO_2H$	3.10	CH_3-CO_2H	4.75
para-$HO_2CC_6H_4-CO_2H$	3.51	$(CH_3)_3C-CO_2H$	5.03

There is a reasonable correlation between maximum electrostatic potential and aqueous pK_a in these compounds.

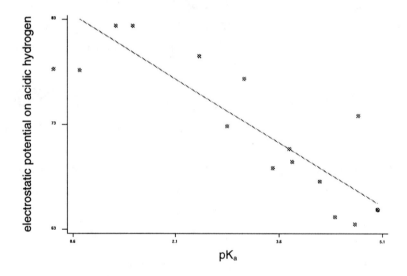

1. E.P. Sargeant and B. Dempsey, **Ionization Constraints of Organic Acids in Aqueous Solution**, IUPAC no. 23, Permagon Press, 1979.

Stereochemistry of Base-Induced Elimination Reactions

Elimination of HX from an alkane or cycloalkane typically follows an E_2 mechanism and occurs with *anti* stereochemistry, e.g., elimination of HCl from chlorocyclohexane.[1]

Labeling studies show, however, that the elimination of HCl from norbornyl chloride in the presence of strong base occurs with *syn* stereochemistry.[2]

The mechanism for elimination in this case probably involves initial deprotonation by *tert*-ButylO$^-$, followed by loss of Cl$^-$.

If the mechanism is correct, it suggests that the *syn* proton in norbornyl chloride is more acidic than the *anti* proton.

A previous application (**Acidities of Carboxylic Acids**) examined the use of electrostatic potential maps to quantify acidities. Another possible indicator of relative acid strength is the absolute value of the lowest-unoccupied molecular orbital (LUMO) mapped onto an electron density surface corresponding to a van der Waals contact surface at each of the possible acidic hydrogens in a neutral molecule. The LUMO indicates the location of positive charge in the acid, that is, the likely location for approach of a base, while the electron density reflects the steric environment presented to the base by the acid.

Within such a model, a base will attempt to **maximize** interaction of its electrons with the LUMO on the acid, and **minimize** interactions with filled orbitals (electron density) on the acid.

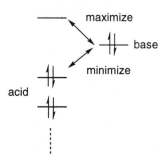

i)   Obtain an equilibrium geometry for norbornyl chloride using semi-empirical AM1 calculations, and follow this by a single energy calculation using the Hartree-Fock 3-21G$^{(*)}$ model. Calculate both electron density and LUMO isosurfaces. Display the former as a mesh or transparent solid, and simultaneously the latter as a solid. Examine the composite graphic in the vicinity of the *syn* and *anti* hydrogens, removal of either of which would give rise to norbornene.

The LUMO at the syn hydrogen in norbornyl chloride is more accessible than the LUMO at the corresponding anti hydrogen.

electron density (transparent) and
LUMO (solid) in norbornyl chloride

This suggests that the syn hydrogen will be more easily approached by a base, leading to syn elimination.

Nortricylane is a minor product in the base-induced elimination of HCl from norbornyl chloride. Are you able to account for this?

ii)   Next, examine the composite graphic to see if you can rationalize formation of nortricyclane. Specifically, look in the vicinity of any hydrogens, removal of which might give rise to nortricyclane.

The composite graphic suggests that the syn hydrogen across the bridgehead from the chlorine should also be accessible to attack by base.

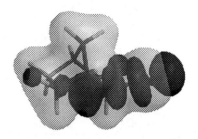

another view of the electron density (transparent)
and LUMO (solid) in norbornyl chloride

Removal of this hydrogen would result in the known formation of nortricyclane.

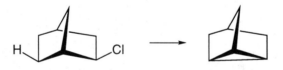

1. For a discussion see: F. A. Carey and R.J. Sundberg, **Advanced Organic Chemistry**, 3rd Ed., Part A, Plenum Press, New York, 1990, p.377.
2. R.A. Bartsch and J.G. Lee, *J. Org. Chem.*, **56**, 212 (1991).

Stereochemistry of Nucleophilic Additions

Nucleophilic addition to asymmetric carbonyl compounds is stereospecific and may be highly stereoselective. For example, most nucleophiles preferentially add to cyclohexanone rings from the more-crowded *axial* face over the less-crowded *equatorial* face.

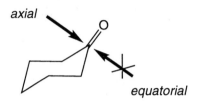

Axial attack is also favored in dioxanone rings but not in dithianone rings.

The best approach of a nucleophile to a substrate is that which **maximizes** interaction of the nucleophile with unfilled orbitals on the substrate, and which **maximizes** interaction of the nucleophile with filled orbitals (electron density) on the substrate.

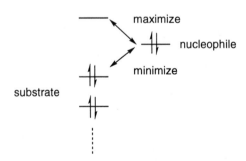

i) Obtain an equilibrium geometry for cyclohexanone using semi-empirical AM1 calculations and follow this by a single energy calculation using the Hartree-Fock 3-21G model. Calculate both electron density and LUMO isosurfaces. Display the former as a transparent solid, and the latter as a solid. Examine the composite graphic on both faces of the carbonyl group.

The LUMO in cyclohexanone is more accessible from the axial face than from the equatorial face.

electron density (transparent) and LUMO (solid) for
axial (left) and *equatorial* (right) faces of cyclohexanone

Nucleophilic attack will occur from the axial direction .

ii)   Perform 3-21G$^{(*)}$ calculations (using AM1 geometries) on 1,3-dioxan-5-one and 1,3-dithian-5-one. Simultaneously display electron density and LUMO surfaces.

The LUMO is more exposed on the axial face in dioxanone and on the equatorial face in dithianone.

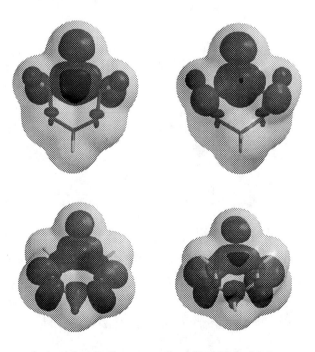

electron density (transparent) and LUMO (solid) for
axial (left) and *equatorial* (right) faces of
1,3-dioxan-5-one (top) and 1,3-dithian-5-one (bottom).

155

LUMO maps (the value of the LUMO mapped onto the electron density surface) provide an alternative (and equivalent) way to elaborate preferences for nucleophilic addition in these systems.

iii)   Calculate and display LUMO maps for cyclohexenone.

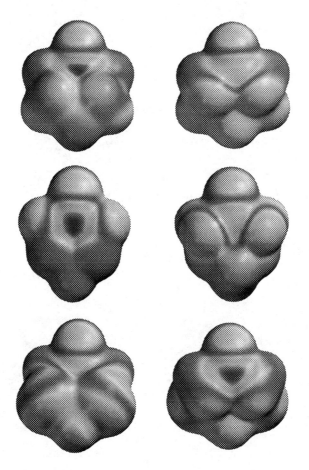

LUMO maps for *axial* (left) and *equatorial* (right)
faces of cyclohexanone (top), 1,3-dioxan-5-one (middle)
and 1,3-dithian-5-one (bottom).

LUMO maps for cyclohexanone, 1,3-dioxan-5-one and 1,3-dithian-5-one show the same preferences toward nucleophilic attack as revealed in the previous composite displays of electron density and LUMO.

Appendix

Common Terms and Acronyms

The page on which the term or acronym is first described is provided in parentheses at the end of each entry.

3-21G. A **Basis Set** in which each inner-shell **Basis Function** is written in terms of three Gaussians, and each valence-shell **Basis Function** is split into two parts, written in terms of two and one Gaussians, respectively. 3-21G is a **Split-Valence Basis Set**. (**19**)

3-21G$^{(*)}$. The **3-21G Basis Set** supplemented by d-type Gaussians for each second-row and heavier main-group element only. 3-21G$^{(*)}$ is a supplemented **Split-Valence Basis Set**. (**21**)

6-31G. A **Basis Set** in which each inner-shell **Basis Function** is written in terms of six Gaussians, and each valence-shell **Basis Function** is split into two parts, written in terms of three and one Gaussians, respectively. 6-31G is a **Split-Valence Basis Set**. (**19**)

6-31G*. The **6-31G Basis Set** in which non-hydrogen atoms are supplemented by d-type Gaussians (**Polarization Functions**). 6-31G* is a **Polarization Basis Set**. (**20**)

6-31G**. A **Basis Set** that is identical to **6-31G*** except that hydrogen atoms are supplemented by p-type Gaussians (**Polarization Functions**). 6-31G** is a **Polarization Basis Set**. (**20**)

6-31+G*. A **Basis Set** that is identical to **6-31G*** except that all non-hydrogen atoms are supplemented by diffuse s and p-type Gaussians (**Diffuse Functions**). 6-31G* is a supplemented **Polarization Basis Set**. (**21**)

6-311G. A **Basis Set** in which each inner-shell **Basis Function** is written in terms of six Gaussians, and each valence-shell **Basis Function** is split into three parts, written in terms of three, one and one Gaussians, respectively. 6-311G is a **Split-Valence Basis Set**. (**19**)

6-311G*. The **6-311G Basis Set** in which non-hydrogen atoms are supplemented by d-type Gaussians (**Polarization Functions**). 6-311G* is a **Polarization Basis Set**. (**20**)

6-311+G**. A **Basis Set** that is identical to **6-311G*** except that non-hydrogen atoms are supplemented by diffuse s and p-type Gaussians (**Diffuse Functions**) and hydrogen atoms are supplemented by p-type Gaussians (**Polarization Functions**). 6-311+G** is a supplemented **Polarization Basis Set**. (**21**)

Ab Initio **Models**. The general term used to describe methods seeking approximate solutions to the many-electron **Schrödinger Equation**, but which do not involve empirical parameters. *Ab initio* models include **Hartree-Fock Models, Møller-Plesset Models** and (some) **Density Functional Models**. (**13**)

Activation Energy. The energy of a **Transition State** above that of reactants. Activation energy is related to reaction rate. (**1**)

AM1. Austin Method **1**. A **Semi-Empirical Model**. (**23**)

Atomic Orbital. A **Basis Function** centered on an atom. Atomic orbitals typically take on the form of the solutions to the hydrogen atom (s, p, d, f... type orbitals). (**13**)

Atomic Units. The set of units which remove all of the constants from inside the **Schrödinger Equation**. The **Bohr** is the atomic unit of length and the **Hartree** is the atomic unit of energy. (**13**)

Basis Functions. Functions usually centered on atoms which are linearly combined to make up the set of **Molecular Orbitals**. (**12**)

Basis Set. The entire collection of **Basis Functions**. (**12**)

Becke-Perdew Model. A **Density Functional Model** which improves on the **Local Density Model** by accounting explicitly for non-uniformity in electron distributions. (**16**)

Bohr. The **Atomic Unit** of length. 1 bohr = 0.529167Å.

Bond Separation Reaction. An *Isodesmic* **Reaction** in which a molecule comprising three or more heavy atoms, and described in terms of a conventional valence structure, is broken down into the simplest (two-heavy-atom) molecules containing the same component bonds. (**112**)

Bond Surface. An **Isodensity Surface** used to elucidate the bonding in molecules. The value of the density is typically taken as 0.1 electrons/**bohr**^{3}. (**134**)

Born-Oppenheimer Approximation. An approximation based on the assumption that nuclei are stationary. Applied to the **Schrödinger Equation**, it leads to the **Electronic Schrödinger Equation**. (**11**)

BP Model; *See* **Becke-Perdew Model**.

BP86 Model; *See* **Becke-Perdew Model**.

Conformation. The arrangement about single bonds and of flexible rings. (**1**)

Correlated Models. Models which take implicit or explicit account of the correlation of electron motions. **MP2 Models** and **Density Functional Models** are correlated models. (**14**)

Correlation; *See* **Electron Correlation**.

Correlation Energy. The difference in energy between the **Hartree-Fock Energy** and the experimental energy. (**14**)

Coulombic Interactions. Charge-charge interactions which follow Coulomb's law. Stabilizing when charges are of opposite sign and destabilizing when they are of the same sign. (**9**)

Density; *See* **Electron Density**.

Density Functional Models. Methods in which the energy is evaluated as a function of the **Electron Density**. **Electron Correlation** is taken into account explicitly by incorporating into the **Hamiltonian** terms which derive from exact solutions of "idealized" many-electron systems. (**15**)

Diffuse Functions. Functions added to a basis set to allow description of electron distributions far away from atomic positions. Important for descriptions of anions. (**21**)

DN*. A **Basis Set** for **Density Functional Models** consisting of numerically-tabulated functions corresponding to solutions of atomic problems. Each inner-shell **Basis Function** is represented by a single function, and each valence-shell **Basis Function** is represented by a pair of functions. Heavy atoms are also provided a set of d-type functions (**Polarization Functions**). DN* is a **Polarization Basis Set**. (**21**)

DN**. A numerical **Basis Set** for **Density Functional Models** that is identical to **DN***, except that hydrogen atoms are also provided p-type function (**Polarization Functions**). DN** is a **Polarization Basis Set**. (**21**)

Electron Correlation. The coupling of electron motions not explicitly taken into account in **Hartree-Fock Models**. (**14**)

Electron Density. The number of electrons per unit volume at a point in space. (**10**)

Electronic Schrödinger Equation. The equation which results from application of the **Born-Oppenheimer Approximation** to the **Schrödinger Equation**. (**11**)

Electrostatic Charges. Atomic charges chosen to best match the **Electrostatic Potential** at points surrounding a molecule, subject to overall charge balance. (**90**)

Electrostatic Potential. A function describing the energy of interaction of a positive point charge with the nuclei and fixed electron distribution of a molecule. (**90**)

Electrostatic Potential Map. A graph that shows the value of **Electrostatic Potential** on an **Electron Density Isosurface** corresponding to a **van der Waals Surface**. (**141**)

Equilibrium Geometry. A **Local Minimum** on a **Potential Energy Surface**. (**1**)

Force Field. The set of rules underlying **Molecular Mechanics Models**. Comprises terms which account for distortions from ideal bond distances and angles and for **Nonbonded van der Waals** and **Coulombic Interactions**. (**9**)

Global Minimum. The lowest energy **Local Minimum** on a **Potential Energy Surface**. (**2**)

Gradient Corrected Density Functional Models; *See* **Non-Local Density Functional Models**.

Hamiltonian. An operator which accounts for the kinetic and potential energy of an atom or a molecule. **(10)**

Hartree. The **Atomic Unit** of energy. 1 hartree = 627.47 kcal/mol.

Hartree-Fock Approximation. Separation of electron motions in many-electron systems into a product form of the motions of the individual electrons. **(12)**

Hartree-Fock Energy. The energy resulting from **Hartree-Fock Models**. **(13)**

Hartree-Fock Equations. The set of coupled differential equations resulting from application of the **Hartree-Fock Approximation** to the many-electron **Schrödinger Equation**. **(12)**

Hartree-Fock Models. Methods in which the many-electron wavefunction in written terms of a product of one-electron wavefunctions. Electrons are assigned in pairs to functions called **Molecular Orbitals**. **(13)**

Hartree-Fock Wavefunction. The simplest quantum-mechanically correct representation of the many-electron wavefunction. Electrons are treated as independent particles and are asigned in pairs to functions termed **Molecular Orbitals**. Also known as **Single-Determinant Wavefunction**. **(12)**

Hessian. The matrix of second energy derivatives with respect to geometrical coordinates. The Hessian together with the atomic masses lead to the **Vibrational Frequencies** of molecular systems. **(2)**

Heterolytic Bond Dissociation. A process in which a bond is broken and a cation and anion result. The number of electron pairs is conserved, but a nonbonding electron pair has been substituted for a bonding electron pair. **(55)**

HOMO. Highest Occupied Molecular Orbital. **(131)**

Homolytic Bond Dissociation. A process in which a bond is broken and two radicals result. The number of electron pairs is not conserved. **(55)**

HOMO Map. A graph that shows the absolute value of the **HOMO** on an **Isodensity Surface** corresponding to a **van der Waals Surface**.

Isodensity Surface. An **Electron Density Isosurface**. It may be used to elucidate bonding or to characterize overall molecular size and shape. **Bond Surfaces** and **Size Surfaces** are isodensity surfaces. **(133)**

Isodesmic **Reaction.** A chemical reaction in which the number of formal chemical bonds of each type is conserved. **(55)**

Isopotential Surface. An **Electrostatic Potential Isosurface**. It may be used to elucidate regions in a molecule which are particularly electron rich and subject to electrophilic attack and those which are particularly electron poor, subject to nucleophilic attack. **(138)**

Isosurface. A three-dimensional surface defined by the set of points in space where the value of the function is constant. **(129)**

Isotope Effect. Dependence of molecular properties and chemical behavior on atomic masses. (**12**)

Isovalue Surface; *See* **Isosurface**.

LCAO Approximation. Linear Combination of Atomic Orbitals approximation. Approximates the unknown **Hartree-Fock Wavefunctions (Molecular Orbitals**) by linear combinations of atom-centered functions (**Atomic Orbitals**) and leads to the **Roothaan-Hall Equations**. (**12**)

Local Density Models. **Density Functional Models** which are based on the assumption that the **Electron Density** is constant (or slowly varying) throughout all space. (**16**)

Local Minimum. Any **Stationary Point** on a **Potential Energy Surface** for which all elements in the diagonal representation of the **Hessian** are positive. (**2**)

Local Spin Density Models; *See* **Local Density Models**.

LUMO. Lowest Unoccupied Molecular Orbital. (**131**)

LUMO Map. A graph that shows the absolute value of the **LUMO** on an **Isodensity Surface** corresponding to a **van der Waals Surface**. (**142**)

Mechanics Models; *See* **Molecular Mechanics Models**.

Merck Molecular Force Field; *See* **MMFF94**.

Minimal Basis Set. A **Basis Set** which contains the fewest functions needed to hold all the electrons on an atom and still maintain spherical symmetry. **STO-3G** is a minimal basis set. (**18**)

MMFF94. Merck Molecular Force Field. A molecular mechanics **Force Field** developed by Merck Pharmaceuticals. Particularly well suited to organic molecules and biopolymers. (**10**)

MNDO. Modified Neglect of Differential Overlap. A **Semi-Empirical Model**. (**22**)

MNDO/d. An extension of the **MNDO Semi-Empirical Model** in which second-row (and heavier) main-group elements are provided a set of d-type functions. (**22**)

Molecular Mechanics Models. Methods for structure, conformation and strain energy calculation based on bond stretching, angle bending and torsional distortions, together with **Nonbonding Interactions**, and parameterized to fit experimental data. (**7**)

Molecular Orbital. A one-electron function made of contributions of **Basis Functions** on individual atoms (**Atomic Orbitals**) and delocalized throughout the entire molecule. (**12**)

Molecular Orbital Models. Methods based on writing the many-electron solution of the **Electronic Schrödinger Equation** in terms of a product of one-electron solutions (**Molecular Orbitals**).

Møller-Plesset Energy. The energy resulting from **Møller-Plesset Models** terminated to a given order, e.g., the MP2 energy is the energy of the second-order Møller-Plesset model (or **MP2**). (**15**)

Møller-Plesset Models. Methods which partially account for **Electron Correlations** by way of the perturbation theory of Møller and Plesset. (**14**)

MP2 Model. A **Møller-Plesset Model** terminated to be second order in the energy. (**15**)

Mulliken Charge. Atom charge obtained from a **Mulliken Population Analysis**. (**90**)

Mulliken Population Analysis. A charge partitioning scheme in which electrons are shared equally between different **Basis Functions**. (**90**)

NDDO Approximation. Neglect of Diatomic Differential Overlap approximation. The approximation underlying all present generation **Semi-Empirical Models**. It says that two atomic orbitals on different atoms do not overlap (see each other). (**22**)

Nonbonded Interactions. Interactions between atoms which are not directly bonded. **van der Waals Interactions** and **Coulombic Interactions** are nonbonded interactions. (**9**)

Non-Local Density Functional Models. Density Functional Models such as the **Becke-Perdew Model** which explicitly take into account electron inhomogeneities. (**16**)

Normal Coordinates. The set of coordinates that lead to a diagonal **Hessian**. Normal coordinates correspond to vibrational motions in molecules.

Normal Mode Analysis. The process for calculating **Normal Coordinates** leading to **Vibrational Frequencies**. This involves diagonalizing the **Hessian** and accounting for atomic masses.

pBP Model. A **Density Functional Model** in which the non-local **Becke-Perdew** correction is introduced pertubatively. (**16**)

PM3. Parameterization Method 3. A **Semi-Empirical Model**. (**22**)

Polarization Basis Set. A **Basis Set** which contains functions of higher angular quantum number (**Polarization Functions**) than required for the ground state of the atom, e.g., p-type functions for hydrogen and d-type functions for main-group elements. **6-31G***, **6-31G**** and **6-311G*** are polarization basis sets. (**20**)

Polarization Functions. Functions of higher angular quantum than required for the ground state atomic description. Added to a basis set to allow displacement of valence-shell **Basis Functions** away from atomic positions. (**20**)

Potential Energy Surface. A many-dimensional function of the energy of a molecule in terms of the geometrical coordinates of the atoms. (**1**)

Property Map. A representation or "map" of a "property" on top of an **Isosurface**, typically an **Isodensity Surface**. **Electrostatic Potential Maps**, and **HOMO** and **LUMO Maps** and **Spin Density Maps** are useful property maps. (**31**)

Quantum Mechanics. Methods based on approximate solution of the **Schrödinger Equation**. (**10**)

Reaction Coordinate. The coordinate that connects the **Local Minima** corresponding to the reactant and product, and which passes through a **Transition State**. (**1**)

Roothaan-Hall Equations. The set of equations describing the best **Hartree-Fock** or **Single-Determinant Wavefunction** within the **LCAO Approximation**. (**13**)

Schrödinger Equation. The quantum mechanical equation which accounts for the motions of nuclei and electrons in atomic and molecular systems. (**10**)

Semi-Empirical Models. Quantum mechanical methods that seek approximate solutions to the many electron **Schrödinger Equation**, but which involve empirical parameters. (**22**)

Single-Determinant Wavefunction; *See* **Hartree-Fock Wavefunction**.

Size Surface. An **Isodensity Surface** used to establish overall molecular size and shape. The value of the density is typically taken as 0.002 electrons/**bohr**^{3}. (**134**).

Spin Density. The difference in the number of electrons per unit volume of "up" spin and "down" spin at a point in space. (**136**)

Spin Density Map. A graph that shows the value of the **Spin Density** on an **Isodensity Surface** corresponding to a **van der Waals Surface**.

Spin Orbital. The form of **Wavefunction** resulting from application of the **Hartree-Fock Approximation** to the **Electronic Schrödinger Equation**. Comprises a space part (**Molecular Orbital**) and one of two possible spin parts ("spin-up" and "spin-down"). (**12**)

Split-Valence Basis Set. A **Basis Set** in which the core region is represented by a single set of **Basis Functions** (a **Minimal Basis Set**) and the valence region is represented by two sets of **Basis Functions**. This allows for description of aspherical atomic environments in molecules. **3-21G**, **6-31G** and **6-311G** are split-valence basis sets. (**19**)

Stationary Point. Any point on a **Potential Energy Surface** for which all energy first derivatives with respect to coordinate changes are zero. **Local Minima** and **Transition States** are stationary points. (**2**)

STO-3G. A **Minimal Basis Set**. Each atomic orbital is written in terms of a sum of three Gaussian functions taken as best fits to Slater-type (exponential) functions. (**18**)

SVWN Model. (Slater, Vosho, Wilk, Nusair) A **Density Functional Model** which involves the **Local Density Approximation**. (**16**)

SYBYL. A molecular mechanics **Force Field** developed by Tripos, Inc. (**9**)

Total Electron Density; *See* **Electron Density**.

Transition State. A **Stationary Point** on a **Potential Energy Surface** in which all but one of the elements in the diagonal representation of the **Hessian** are positive, and one element is negative. This corresponds to the highest-energy point on the **Reaction Coordinate**. (**2**)

Transition State Geometry. The geometry (bond lengths and angles) of a **Transition State**. (**1**)

van der Waals Interactions. Interactions which account for short-range repulsion of nonbonded atoms as well as for weak long-range attraction. (**9**)

van der Waals Radius. The radius of an atom (in a molecule), which is intended to reflect its overall size.

van der Waals Surface. A surface formed by a set of interpreting spheres (atoms) with specific **van der Waals radii**, and which is intended to represent overall molecular size and shape.

Vibrational Frequencies. The energies at which molecules vibrate. Vibrational frequencies orrespond to the peaks in an infrared and Raman spectrum. (**1**)

Wavefunction. The solution of the **Schrödinger Equation**. In the case of the hydrogen atom, a function of the coordinates which describes the motion of the electron as fully as possible. In the case of a many-electron system a function which describes the motion of the individual electrons. (**10**)

Zero Point Energy. The energy due to molecular vibration at 0K. Equal to half the sum of the **Vibrational Frequencies** times Planck's constant.

Index

Note: items in **bold type** refer to page numbers for tables.

A

Ab initio models; *See* Hartree-Fock models

Acidities, performance of different
models **67**

Activation energies
    choice of geometry **108**
    effect of correlation on 84
    performance of different models **82**
    regio and stereochemistry **89**
    substituent effects on **86**

AM1 23

Anomeric effect 71,**74**

Atomic charges
    electrostatic 90
    Mulliken 90

Atomic orbitals 13

B

Basicities, performance of different models . **68**

Basis functions 12

Basis sets
    3-21G 19
    3-21G$^{(*)}$ 21
    6-31G 19
    6-31G* 20
    6-31G** 20
    6-31+G* 21
    6-311G 19
    6-311G* 20
    6-311+G** 21
    DN* 21
    DN** 21
    for semi-empirical models 22
    for use in density functional
    calculations 21
    incorporating diffuse functions 21

    minimal 18
    numerical 21
    polarization 20
    split-valence 19
    STO-3G 18

Bond dissociation energies, homolytic
    effect of correlation on **56**
    performance of different models **58**

Bond separation energies
    choice of geometry **105**
    performance of different models **64**
    use to determine heats of
    formation 112,**114**

Bond surface 134

Bond surface, for
    cyclohexanone 134
    diborane 135
    transition state for pyrolysis of
    ethyl formate 135

Born-Oppenheimer approximation 11

C

Computation times for different models 94,**95**

Conformational energy differences
    choice of geometry **111**
    performance of different models ... 72,**74**

Conformational searching, available
methods 109

Correlated models
    BP models 16
    density functional models 15
    local spin density models 16
    Møller-Plesset models 14
    MP2 models 15
    Need for d functions in basis set 40
    pBP models 17
    SVWN models 16

165

Correlation
    effect on activation energies **83,86,88**
    effect on bond dissociation energies.. 56,**59**
    effect on conformational energy
    differences **73,75**
    effect on dipole moments 91,**93**
    effect on equilibrium geometries
    .... 37,**39,43,45,47,51**
    effect on reaction energetics
    .... **59,60,63,65,67,69**
    effect on transition-state geometries ... **81**
    functional 16

D

Density functional calculations,
    numerical errors 17

Density functional models
    Becke-Perdew 16
    BP 16
    comparison of performance of pBP
    and BP models 23,**24,25,26,27,29**
    comparison of performance with
    numerical and Gaussian basis sets
    .... 28,**30,31,32,34**
    local 16
    non-local 16
    pBP 17
    SVWN 16

Diffuse functions; *See* Basis sets,
incorporating diffuse functions

Dipole moments
    choice of geometry **106**
    effect of correlation on 91
    performance of different models **92**

E

Electric dipole moments; *See* Dipole
moments

Electron correlation; *See* Correlation

Electron density 10,133

Electron density isosurface; *See* Isodensity
Surface

Electronic Schrödinger equation 11

Electrostatic charges; *See* Atomic charges,
electrostatic

Electrostatic potential 90,138

Electrostatic potential, of
    benzene 138,140
    dimethyl ether 139
    fluoromethane 139
    pyridine 138
    trimethylamine 139

Electrostatic potential map 141

Electrostatic potential map, for
    β-alanine 141
    benzene 140,148
    benzyl cation 141
    cytosine 146
    guanine 146
    transition state for pyrolysis of ethyl
    formate 142

Equilibrium geometries, performance of
different models, for
    anions **46**
    cations **46**
    hydrocarbons **38**
    hydrogen-bonded complexes **50**
    molecules incorporating heteroatoms . **42**
    molecules incorporating second-row
    elements **44**
    transition-metal carbonyls **52**
    transition-metal organometallics **53**

Exchange functional 16

F

Force fields; *See* MMFF94, SYBYL

Fourier series, for describing torsion energy . 8

G

Gaussian functions.................................. 18

Geometries; *See* Equilibrium geometries

H

Hartree-Fock approximation 12

Hartree-Fock energy 13

Hartree-Fock equations 12

Hartree-Fock models 13

Hartree-Fock wavefunction 12

Heats of formation,from bond separation
reactions 112,**114**

HOMO 131

HOMO, of
    cis-1,3-butadiene 131
    ethene 131
    sulfur tetrafluoride 132

Homolytic bond dissociation energies; *See*
Bond dissociation energies, homolytic

Hydrogen-bonded complexes; *See*
Equilibrium geometries, hydrogen-bonded
systems

Hydrogenation energies, performance
of different models **60**

Hypervalent molecules 21

I

Isodensity surface 133

Isodesmic reactions 55

Isomerization energies
    choice of geometry **103**
    performance of different models **62**

Isopotential surface 138

Isosurface 129

Isotope effects 12,136

Isovalue surface; *See* Isosurface

L

LCAO approximation 12

Linear combinations of atomic orbitals
approximation; *See* LCAO approximation

Local density models; *See* Density functional
models, local

LUMO 131

LUMO of
    benzyl cation 132
    cyclohexanone 155
    1,3-dioxan-5-one 155

    1,3-dithian-5-one 155
    ethene 131
    norbornyl chloride 152,153

LUMO map 142

LUMO map, for
    cyclohexenone 143,156
    1,3-dioxan-5-one 156
    1,3-dithian-5-one 156
    methylcyclohexenone 144

M

MMFF94 10

MNDO 22

MNDO/d 22

Molecular mechanics models 7

Molecular orbitals 12,130

Møller-Plesset energy, second order 15

Møller-Plesset models 14

MP2 models 15

Mulliken charges; *See* Atomic Charges,
Mulliken

Mulliken population analysis 90

N

NDDO approximation 22

Nonbonded interactions 9

P

Performance of different models,
overview 97,**98**

PM3 22

Polarization functions; *See* Basis sets,
polarization

Population analysis; *See* Mulliken
population analysis

Potential energy surface 1

Potential map; *See* Electrostatic potential
map

Property map 129

Proton affinities; *See* Basicities

R

Reaction types **54**

Roothaan-Hall equations 13

S

Schrödinger equation 10

Semi-empirical models 22

Semi-empirical models, parameterization
of 22

Single-determinant wavefunction 12

Size surface 134

Size surface, for
    ammonia 136
    benzene 140
    cyclohexanone 134,155
    1,3-dioxan-5-one 155
    1,3-dithian-5-one 155
    hydronium cation 136
    methyl anion 136
    norbornyl chloride 152,153

SPARTAN 6,21,76,94,**95**,129,136

Spin density 136

Spin density, for allyl radical 137

Spin orbital 12

SVWN models; *See* Density functional
models, SVWN

SYBYL 9

T

Thermodynamic properties, effect of
choice of geometry on 104

Times; *See* Computation times

Total electron density; *See* Electron density

Transition state energies; *See* Activation
energies

Transition state geometries, from
different models **80**

V

Vibrational frequencies, choice of
equilibrium geometries for 104

W

Wavefunction 10

Woodward-Hoffmann rules 130

X

X-ray diffraction, relationship to
electron density 10,133

168

Wavefunction Publications

The Molecular Modeling Workbook for Organic Chemistry $ 29.95
(full color workbook + CDROM) W.J. Hehre, A.J. Shusterman, J.E. Nelson, 1998
(ISBN 1-890661-06-6)

Practical Strategies for Electronic Structure Calculations $ 25.00
W.J. Hehre, 1995
(ISBN 0-9643495-1-5)

A Laboratory Book of Computational Organic Chemistry $ 25.00
W.J. Hehre, A.J. Shusterman, W.W. Huang, 1996
(ISBN 0-9643495-5-8)

A Short Course in Modern Electronic Structure Methods $150.00
(spiral bound lecture notes), W.J. Hehre, 1993-1997

An Even Shorter Course in Modern Electronic Structure Methods $ 50.00
(spiral bound lecture notes), W.J. Hehre, 1996-1998

Molecular Modeling in Undergraduate Chemistry Education $ 25.00
(spiral bound lecture notes), W.J. Hehre, W.W. Huang, A.J. Shusterman, 1996-1998

A Brief Guide to Molecular Mechanics and Quantum Chemical Calculations $ 25.00
W.J. Hehre, J. Yu, P.E. Klunzinger, L. Lou, 1998
(ISBN 1-890661-05-8)

A SPARTAN Tutorial $ 20.00
W.J. Hehre, W.W. Huang, P.E. Klunzinger, B.J. Deppmeier, A.J. Driessen, 1997
(ISBN 1-890661-00-7)

SPARTAN User's Guide $ 35.00
(ISBN 1-890661-02-3)

MacSPARTAN User's Guide and Tutorial $ 35.00
(ISBN 0-9643495-4-X)

MacSPARTAN *Plus* Tutorial and User's Guide $ 35.00
(ISBN 0-9643495-7-4)

PC SPARTAN Tutorial and User's Guide $ 35.00
(ISBN 0-9643495-6-6)

PC SPARTAN *Plus* Tutorial and User's Guide $ 35.00
(ISBN 1-890661-03-1)

A PC SPARTAN *Pro* Tutorial $ 20.00
W.J. Hehre, W.W. Huang, P.E. Klunzinger, B.J. Deppmeier, 1998
(ISBN 1-890661-08-2)

PC SPARTAN *Pro* User's Guide $ 35.00
(ISBN 1-890661-09-0)

Wavefunction, Inc.
18401 Von Karman Ave., Ste. 370, Irvine, CA 92612 USA
Phone: (949) 955-2120 • Fax: (949) 955-2118
books@wavefun.com • http://www.wavefun.com